# HOME FOR CHRISTMAS
# AND OTHER STORIES

# Home
# for
# Christmas

*and other stories*

# SCOTT
# YOUNG

Illustrated by Huntley Brown

A Young & Hogan Book for
**Macmillan of Canada**
*A Division of Canada Publishing Corporation*
Toronto, Ontario, Canada

All inquiries regarding the motion picture or other dramatic
rights for this book should be addressed to the author's and
Young & Hogan Publishing's representative, MGA Agency Inc.,
303 Davenport Road, Toronto, Ontario, Canada, M5R 1K5.
Representations as to the disposition of these rights are strictly
prohibited without express written consent and will be
vigorously pursued to the full extent of the law.

Many of these stories appeared originally in a slightly different
form in The Globe and Mail. The Second Coming of Ordinary
Angel Blobs is an updated version of a naval yarn the author
heard in 1944, while serving with the Royal Navy in the Adriatic.

**Canadian Cataloguing in Publication Data**
Young, Scott, 1918-
    Home for Christmas and other stories

ISBN 0-7715-9633-2

I.  Title.

PS8547.07H65 1989      C813'.54      C89-094222-6
PR9199.3.Y6H65 1989

Design: Bruce Lepper

A Young & Hogan Publishing Book for
**Macmillan of Canada**
A Division of Canada Publishing Corporation
Toronto, Ontario, Canada

Typesetting by Heritage Publications, Peterborough, Ontario
Printed in the United States of America
on acid-free paper

*For my children, including my stepdaughter Maggie,*
*who first collected some of these stories*
*as Christmas gifts for the family, and their children.*

# CONTENTS

# ONCE UPON A TIME
# IN TORONTO

Once upon a time in Toronto, there was a young couple, he 22 and she 23, who came from some distant place just a few weeks before Christmas. They found a one-room apartment in an old building on Robina Avenue, which runs north of St. Clair just past Oakwood in the west end.

They had no furniture except a gate-leg table, a bridge table with folding chairs, and a tea-wagon that had been wedding presents when they married a few months before. The apartment had a bed that could be raised on its end and locked into place between closet doors in the morning, and let down the same way at night. When it was down, it blocked the entrance to the bathroom, but it was no trouble and even giggling fun to walk across the bed when that was the case.

In the basement hallway of the old apartment building was a sofa whose upholstery had been painted maroon with ordinary house paint. It was waiting to be hauled away with the garbage but the woman, who had dark hair and brown eyes, got the janitor's permission to move it into the apartment.

The little kitchen had the only window in the place that would open. They got used to the scratch of steel wheels as the high TTC trolleys short-turned right under the window on what was called the Robina Loop. He made $25 a week, which worked out to about $22 after deductions. They paid $30 a month for the apartment. They had about $15 a week for carfare, food and other expenses.

That was okay until suddenly Christmas was upon them. As they were newly married, they had never had Christmas together. They bought a few cards and small presents to send away to their parents. When that was done they had nothing left from that week's pay.

His job was nights, from 6 p.m. to 2 a.m. He had to work on Christmas Eve. They talked about a Christmas tree but when they walked around the district trees were $2 and up, more than they could afford.

It didn't bother them. They had enough in other ways. But on Christmas Eve before he caught the St. Clair car to go to work they were out for their usual afternoon walk when they found tree prices had dropped. On one lot, trees were being cleared at 50 cents.

They looked at each other, then took a long time to choose. She wanted a small, fat tree and she found one. He borrowed a hammer and nails from the janitor and made a wooden stand from an old packing case. They had it up in late afternoon of Christmas Eve, without decorations. They put the tree in a corner by an old sizzling radiator and laid their few parcels under it, one parcel being a pipe, for him, and another a nightgown, for her, both to be surprises, of course.

They ate at four o'clock as usual so he could get to work on time. He went off with two tuna-fish and onion sandwiches she had made for his mid-evening lunch. Snow was falling outside the streetcar windows. He could see people on the streets carrying parcels, trudging through the snow in the yellow of the street lights. Sometimes the car he was on, going downtown almost empty, would stop beside one coming the other way, loaded to the doors with people dimly seen through steamy windows, chatting, juggling parcels, all with a kind of busy Christmas Eve glow.

That night he was not busy at his office, where he wrote wire-service stories picked up from the daily papers. All across the country, newspapers were shutting down early. He was told he could leave at midnight. There was nothing left to do. He and the people he worked with called out their Merry Christmases and he took the streetcar home. The night was very quiet as he walked through the snow the last block to the apartment. There were fewer outdoor decorations in those days, but in windows he could see outlines of decorated trees and thought, next year we'll have decorations, too.

When he tapped on the door and she opened it and he stepped in, he could hardly believe the look of the tree. It was hung for all of its short fatness with little rosettes made of white and red tissue paper. She had worked on it all evening, tying handfuls of leftover wrappings with white wool and clipping the ends with scissors to make them look like petals.

When they went to bed the glow from the street-light outside shone on the little tree. They lay there and looked at it for a while and then she said, "There's an envelope on the tree that I want you to open now." He found it and turned on a light to read it. "This is our first Christmas," he read. "We don't have much except each other, but I have cut up little bits of my heart for you, to put on our first tree."

For nearly 20 years after that, those first decorations always had a place among the grander and grander ones on their trees. And he remembers them yet, long after their marriage broke up, and knows that so does she.

# RED WAGON

When Kip wakened that morning, he could hear his mother and father tip-toeing around at the door whispering. This was strange. Usually when he wakened there was no noise until he made it. Then he would yell, "Morneen!" a few times until his father, in rumpled pyjamas, with hair hanging over his half-closed eyes, would come in and carry Kip to the bathroom. His father then would stand with eyes closed. When Kip was finished, his father would return him to his crib and mumble, "Go back to sleep." Then his father would disappear and no matter how much noise Kip made it was always another hour before he could get one of them up again, although often they would yell, "Shut up!"

But this time there were whispers. Kip sat up carefully in his crib and listened.

"Hear anything?" one whisper asked.

"No," said the other whisper. "Must be still asleep."

"Just like a kid," said the first whisper. "Gad. Gets up early every morning but Christmas." Kip's father said Gad a lot.

"If he knew what was out here, he'd be up all right," said the first whisper again.

Kip became mildly excited. This was interesting, but he couldn't sit around all day in bed when there was the bathroom. This was important. Sometimes he didn't make it on time.

"Morne-e-e-n!" he called.

The door opened quickly. They were standing there. His mother had washed her face, which was not usual at this time of morning. His father had combed his hair.

They both said Merry Christmas, whatever that meant. Kip contemplated the word, or two words, whatever it was, and kept silent. He knew he'd just make a fool of himself if he tried to say it, or them, back, although that was obviously expected of him. He stood up in bed.

"Red Wagon!" he commanded. "Red Wagon!"

"Bathroom first," said his mother.

"Gad. Wait'll he sees that other stuff," said his father, who was smiling. This, in Kip's experience, was unparalleled. It wasn't that his father wasn't a nice man. But he usually just didn't seem happy in the morning.

In the bathroom, Kip repeated his earlier request. "Red Wagon!" he said, even more insistently. The odd atmosphere around here this morning unnerved him, slightly. He tried to say that but it came out funny and they didn't understand. Kip shrugged. No harm in trying.

What was up? They still hadn't brought him Red Wagon. He took his time, thinking about Red Wagon. His mother and father stood impatiently before him, his mother holding Kip's dressing gown. Red Wagon was a wagon that his father had made for him. The box part was just big enough to hold four blocks. He thought it was four. More than two, anyway. The wheels were made of wooden spools. It had a string on the front, for pulling.

"Red Wagon," he demanded. "Uh, Red Wagon."

"It's Christmas," said his mother, as if that explained everything. Kip couldn't figure out this Christmas stuff. They'd been talking about it for days. On the radio some man came on and talked about a book in which he kept track of when children were bad. This apparently had some bearing on his business. Either his name was Santa Claus or that was who he worked for. Every once in a while he laughed like a madman. Kip preferred another radio program he often heard which featured a small song, "Shop at Albert's Hardware Store." Kip had once been into a hardware store, and to him that program made sense.

As far as he knew, he'd never had any contact with this Claus.

"Red Wagon," he said again, from his seat on the toilet. He was getting nowhere.

"Finnst," he said.

His mother and father looked at each other in awe. "He said 'finnst'," said his mother. "Must mean finished."

"Lat does mean finnst," confirmed Kip.

They got him off and into his dressing gown. They wouldn't let him go back to his room for Red Wagon. They each took one hand and then all walked together the length of the bungalow to the living room.

Gad! A tree. With lights on it. And parcels all

around. Kip sized up a couple of the parcels on the basis of their suitability to be carried in Red Wagon. Not one of them was small enough. Still, it was a nice-looking tree. He said as much, whereupon his father and mother grinned at each other again.

It turned out that the system was this. Kip sat in his own small chair over by the radiator. His mother sat on the chesterfield. His father picked up each present, shook it, read the label, and then handed it either to Kip or Kip's mother or left it on a pile at his own side.

Kip was hungry.

He fingered one of the parcels he'd got, but it was hard and bore no resemblance to anything to eat. In some ways, other mornings were better. Even with all the rushing around and the banging of the bathroom door, breakfast was served promptly. Today they didn't seem to care if they ever ate. Or fed anybody else, for that matter.

"All finished," said his father.

"Open your presents now, Kippy," said his mother.

Kip tore the paper off a parcel. It was round, like a clock, only it had a red face painted on it and a gadget sticking out of the bottom. Kip pulled. Nothing happened. Then he pushed. There was a loud spluttering noise and the eyes in this face shot fire and Kip dropped it like a spoonful of hot pablum. Gad!

"Gad!" said his father. "Quite a toy!"

Kip was astonished. That, a toy? He wouldn't like to meet that thing alone in a dark crib.

He unwrapped another parcel. A monkey apparently ran up and down this string. Interesting, but . . . Gad! What's this? A duck. Kip got up and pulled the string thoughtfully. The duck's feet waddled. It reminded him of Red Wagon.

"Red Wagon," he said hopefully.

His parents looked a little disappointed. He unwrapped more parcels. A few sweaters and stuff like that. Then a parcel that squeaked. When he was unwrapping it, he felt apprehensive. He didn't like the squeak. He finally got the paper off. A dumb-looking rabbit. Rubber. He pushed it. It squeaked. He threw it on the floor. It squeaked again.

One more parcel left.

It squeaked, too! Kip threw it on the floor. His mother picked it up and unwrapped it. A rubber donkey. Kip refused to hold it.

Both big people looked worried, now, but apparently decided to have one more try. They lifted Kip down to the floor among all his presents. They knelt beside him. His father made the monkey run up the string. His mother made the wild face flash and splutter. Together they squeaked the rubber rabbit and the rubber donkey.

Kip screamed. He knew it was going to be a good scream when he started, but he hadn't known it would be that good. He screamed again and knew that both were fine, ringing screams.

They started back, woe-stricken. All the noises had ceased. He stopped screaming.

"Nose," he said.

They blew his nose.

"Red Wagon," he said.

His father ran down the hall and got Red Wagon. Kip took it, gingerly skirted the pile of squeaks, sparks and waddles, and sat down on the floor with Red Wagon.

His father and mother opened their parcels but at first they were only half-looking at the presents, watching him curiously.

"He was confused by all the things, all at once," his mother said.

"It'll be better next year," his father said. "Then he'll be nearly three. He'll know what it's all about."

I hope so, thought Kip. But, in the meantime, I wish we'd eat. He got up and went out into the kitchen, dragging Red Wagon.

# LITTLE STARS
# OF BETHLEHEM

And so it came to pass that in the little country school (when these were still in style) the Christmas concert was planned as usual for Christmas Eve.

This was not considered a stupid idea, as it might be in some communities, because here it was a long-held custom.

From experience, people knew that the concert would end early enough for them to hang up stockings and do the last-minute wrapping. And in the community also it had been found that when a man knew he was going to face his neighbors and the neighbor children on Christmas Eve he tended to limit severely his stay at the beer parlor on the way home.

Everybody arrived at the little school at about the same time, 7 p.m.: Joseph, Mary, the shepherds, the parents, the wise men, the kids too little to go to school, the rhythm band, carol chorus, and the old people who had grandchildren in the concert (and had been in it themselves, long ago).

The costumes were all the responsibility of the players. Therefore, they depended a good deal on such matters as which homes had sewing machines, and which mothers had the time or the talent – or even

whether a child had thought to tell anybody at home that he was in the show, and needed a costume, before the last minute.

This was apparent in one conversation as all hands milled about in the foyer, saying Merry Christmas. The shepherds were shoving and tickling each other. The mother of one had worked all week on his outfit, and he looked like a gorgeous bit player from an old Cecil B. De Mille Bible western, while the other shep-

herds were dressed in superannuated dressing gowns, with towels for turbans, if any.

And the father of the well-dressed shepherd drew him aside and worriedly said unto him: "Does it bother you to be in such a fancy outfit when all the other shepherds aren't?"

The boy shrugged. "So? I'm a rich shepherd, that's all."

The schoolroom was nicely decorated. The Christmas tree stood in a mound of parcels just large enough to warm the cockles of the most frosty-hearted crayon manufacturer. A red curtain was strung on a wire across one end of the room. Behind it was great activity, while out in front the parents and grandparents sat on chairs and gazed stolidly into the eyes of lap-sized children looking stolidly over the shoulders of their mothers from the row in front.

A man named Bud was master of ceremonies. His youngest son, in red corduroy overalls bulging sveltely over his diaper, provided the first nice comic touch by wandering out behind him and standing, thumb in mouth, gazing at the audience, while Bud made the opening announcement.

One early highlight was the rhythm band and carol chorus. Eighteen little people stood in a row, all smiles and without a front tooth between the lot of them, whanging away (or staring at the audience and forgetting to whang) at triangles, sticks and drums. A little drummer boy (tum-tee-tum-tum) hit his thumb a real belt, and sucked it solemnly through the rest of their first piece.

Then it was time for Richard's solo. Richard was in Grade 4. As he walked to the front in his neat blue suit, white shirt, bow tie, and brown shoes, fair hair slicked down, a woman murmured, "That takes real courage." You could tell she was right. Richard had screwed-up courage sticking out all over him.

And then as he bowed and the piano played its first bars, and Richard took a deep breath, the entire 18-piece rhythm band and carol chorus charged through the curtain and past him to the remaining seats. This took a while, but seemed to calm Richard, having someone else the cynosure of all eyes. He sang very well. So did Wendy, in her solo.

It was after Wendy bolted for her seat beside her mother that Monica, the curtain puller, drew a big laugh. The play was on next. The chorus was ready to file in. Monica walked across the room haughtily pulling on the curtain so that the people in the play could take up their positions. But she did not notice that the curtain failed to spread out behind her. The little bunch of red curtain just moved across the room with her and left bare all the hustling prop-men hurrying onstage and then stopping to gape at the audience, holding mangers and armfuls of straw.

Nevertheless, the chorus again sang beautifully, a tribute to Mr. Bush, the music teacher and conductor, who was known to children and parents alike as Wild Bill Bush.

When the curtain was fixed, and later re-opened, the stable scene had been screened from view and the audience could see a crowd of shepherds, no doubt watching their flocks by night.

They also were palavering about news they had heard: that a Christ-child had been born, and that wise men from afar were bringing rich gifts of Frank-in-Cents and mur-r-r-r. While they palavered they leaned on their crooks, one of which had a screw-in end where a mop had been. Some argued, how did they know a Christ-child had been born anyway? And others wondered what gift they had to give Him if He had been.

The argument seemed to have reached an impasse when in burst a traveller dressed in a burlap sack, bow tie, snowboots, and with a Paisley scarf wrapped around his head. He was straight from Bethlehem, he said, and confirmed the good news.

Whereupon the shepherds trooped offstage and when the curtain opened again it showed them crowding around the manger, and the well-dressed shepherd was on one knee giving quite a natural gift, considering his profession.

"It's only a little gray lamb," he said, "but it's the only lamb we got."

# THE SECOND COMING OF ORDINARY ANGEL BLOBS

**M**any mysterious events occur, or seem to occur, in the Christmas season, but the most mysterious in recent times happened this year in and around Halifax. It was almost as if a Greater Power looked down upon the navies of what used to be the British Empire, hunting for just the right situation, and then exclaimed, "Gor-blimey!" and did a cosmic double-take at the sight of an ancient Bangor-class mine-sweeper ploughing along in heavy seas, approaching Halifax harbor. Tapping a key on His video display screen, He found that 16 of Canada's 20 destroyers had been ordered tied up because of cracks in their aged boilers, and as a result smaller ships such as this Bangor, now 40 years old, had been recommissioned temporarily.

The Bangors were quite familiar to Him, playing as He did the title role in Eternal Father, strong to save, whose hand doth guide the restless wave, and otherwise trying to make things as comfy as possible for those in peril on the sea. He had almost forgotten the way the waves broke over a Bangor's unflared bows, causing a steady groaning chorus of, "Here comes a green one!" from those on deck, a green one, of course, being the seagoing term for solid water breaking over a ship's bow. "Just the ruddy thing for Blobs," He said.

A couple of hours later, the Bangor was tied up and its pale and shaken crew sinking into harbor routine when a small and bow-legged sailor walked through the dockyard gates and along the jetty. It was 14 days before Christmas and raining hard in Halifax (you could look it up). The rain pelted down on a uniform that no one watching had seen for years, bouncing off the round cap and soaking the bell-bottomed blue serge trousers below the long blue greatcoat. The small sailor's eyes swept slowly from end to end of the Bangor. Then, as the sub-lieutenant at the gangway later recalled, he distinctly heard the little sailor mutter, "'Ell is bloody right."

At the same instant, the captain in his cabin was reading an unexpected signal just in, stating that an able seaman named Blobs would report forthwith on loan from the Royal Navy for temporary duty. When the gangway subbie rang up the captain he was given this word, so directed Blobs forward to the seamen's mess. Everyone there later recalled that Blobs just seemed to materialize among them. Stewart was reading a lurid paperback, Wojciechowski using china cement to mend a cup broken in the storm outside, Putnam pressing the trousers of his Number One green uniform, Blore writing a letter, others asleep. They looked up to see this little sailor glaring at them disgustedly before, throwing his huge seabag to the deck, he roared, "I thought that wet subbie didn't

know wot the 'ell 'e was doin' – where in 'ell's the seamen's mess, so I can get me 'ead down?''

Wojciechowski said stiffly, "This is the seamen's mess."

"Then w'y isn't ye dressed like seamen?"

"We is! I mean, we are!" Blore said. "Ya never seen a Canadian sailor before, ya dummy? Where'd ya get that outfit you're in, Malabar's?"

"Canadian!" Blobs said. "Oh. All right, then, where does I sling me mick?"

"Mick?" said Blore, who was old enough to remember hammocks. "We don't use hammocks here. Bunks." He gestured to two or three empty bunks.

"I'll use me mick," Blobs muttered, reaching into his seabag and bringing out a tightly rolled hammock which he expertly slung between two bunks. He crawled in, one short bowed leg out on either side for balance, closed his eyes, and slept. "He's come a long way," Blore said, not knowing how right he was.

They had scarcely fuelled a few hours later when a tinny voice bawled from the loudspeaker over their heads, "Stations for leaving harbor!" As they scrambled for oilskins and boots Blobs scrambled with them and amazingly was first on deck. The word went around the ship that a trawler was in trouble up the coast. Out in the open water the waves broke over the bow as they always did, drenching everyone except those on the bridge, which was enclosed. Blobs, soaked, did everything as swiftly and expertly as he had slung his hammock. Two days later when they returned, the trawler in tow, everyone on the lower decks knew that whatever they knew about the sea, Blobs knew more. When one man hit by a wave had been smashed against a bulkhead and broke his arm, Blobs was first to reach him. When another man lost his grip on a safety line and might have been washed overboard, Blobs got to him holding the line with one hand and the man with the other, until he got his grip again.

In fact, when entering harbor all hands were willing to concede that he was the best seaman any of them had ever seen, the most experienced, the most travelled, until suddenly through the fog appeared the mighty towering legs and platform of Petrocan's ocean-going drilling rig looking like a monstrous, menacing waterbug and held firmly in mid-stream by anchors that weighed 30,000 tons each.

At the sight Blobs reeled back as if from fright, "Wot in the bloody 'ell's that?" he gasped.

"Drilling rig," Smitty answered, looking at him strangely. Everybody at sea saw those things now. Bloody ocean was full of them.

A terrible 11 days followed: four more times to sea, during which admiration for Blobs grew. He took everything as if he had it coming to him, somehow, and was determined not to holler uncle, or any other non-swear word. But finally Christmas morning came. They'd all had a skinful and then a good sleep and began to ask questions.

"Tell us, Uncle Blobs," said Blore, "how'd you ever qualify for a draft to this high-class ship?"

"Get yer 'ead down," Blobs said.

"Come on, Blobsy," said Smitty, a long-service man, in since the early 1960s, "sending a seaman with your experience to this tub is like sending bloody Admiral Nelson to chip paint on an armed yacht."

"Get yer 'ead down," said Blobs, his faded blue eyes on the painted round knobs of the bulkhead rivets a foot from his thin leathery face.

"How did you come here, Blobs?" asked Gareth Fowler-Homfray, who was nearly bald and looked rather gentlemanly except for the name of a ship, Skeena, tattooed on his right biceps. "I mean, you're obviously a man from the big ones, the battlers and cruisers and carriers. And we hear you're only aboard this one for a short posting ... "

"Fourteen days," said Blobs. "It's up tomorrow."

"But how come 14 days?" asked Fowler-Homfray.

Blobs swung his legs in and turned on his side and raised himself on one elbow. Not everyone can even lie still on a Navy hammock, let alone turn on his side or raise himself on one elbow. He gazed along the crowded messdeck, the lockers strewn with clothes, clean and dirty, some being used as pillows by seamen who had got their heads down, but were listening.

"Let's hear it, Blobs," Barton said.

Smitty said, "What was your last ship, Blobsy?"

"The 'eavy cruiser Repulse," said Blobs.

"Ah!" Smitty exploded, laughing, "you're not that old!" Smitty had been a baby then, but had heard of Repulse. "Repulse was sunk away back in ... "

"Forty-two," Blobs said. "Early bloody forty-two."

"I don't believe it," Smitty laughed, "but I'll go along with the gag. You were saved, of course, discovered the fountain of youth, and 40 years later you lied about your age and got back in ... "

"No," said Blobs. "I weren't saved, ya crud! And I'll tell you 'ow it 'appened as long as none among yez interrupts, or laughs at me 'orrid plight, or makes any bloody sound whatever."

There was a chorus of promises to keep silent. Blobs glared suspiciously around and his tone was properly mournful as he went on to tell them the story they insisted on hearing, namely, 'ow 'e came to come 'ere:

Repulse was off the coast of Malaya, steaming north in company with the battleship Prince of Wales (said Blobs) when the Jap aircraft seen us. The torpedo planes came at us like flocks of bloody starlings. I won't tell yez 'ow 'eroic wc was, tryin' to fight 'em off, because we got sunk, and ye can't be a proper 'ero, gettin' sunk. Me action station in Repulse was the B-gun ammo hoist. One minute I'm there and then there's a mighty bloody pow and the next minute I'm queued up at the Pearly Gates with a lot of other Navy blokes and soon I gets me turn in front of this Leadin' Angel, Peter.

"Name?" 'e says.

"Able Seaman Blobs," I answers.

"All take a drop in ratin' 'ere," 'e says. "Henceforward until cause be shown for promotion you take the rate of Ordinary Angel, Blobs," 'e says. "Next!"

It looks fine around there, inside, it do – mighty bloody marble 'alls, messdecks where ye does nothin' but eat and sleep, not eat and sleep and write letters and mend cups, too, like this one. And when ye draws yer tot the Petty Angel at the spirit locker ain't keepin' 'is thumb in the rum ladle tryin' to save 'alf the day's spirits for the petty angels' mess, either, like every other ship I been in. When I slings me mick that night I know it can't last and I'll find meself standin' lookout on some wet cloud all night, back to bloody normal. But meantime I likes it fine.

Next day it's just like 'arbor routine. Petty Angel comes around shoutin' wakey-wakey at oh-six-three-oh, 'ands to breakfast a 'alf hour later, out pipes at oh-seven-five-five, 'ands fall in at oh-eight-'undred. And then I finds that standin' lookout on a wet cloud ain't the worst that can 'appen to Ordinary Angel Blobs.

After we'd fell in – I'm in the middle, well 'id – the Leadin' Angel stands out front and gives us a talk about some of the new angels from small ships (Blobs glared around) bein' careless about shinin' boots and such. Then 'e points to company's port side and says, "Them uns there, clean Creator's galley," and the port-siders doubles off to work. Then 'e points to starboard and says, "Them uns there, clean Creator's cabin," and they doubles off.

"Rest," 'e says. "'Arpin'!"

Right there's where I makes me big mistake. I figures drawin' 'arps must be akin to drawin' brooms or mops or anythin' else in the Navy and if I falls in at the end of the line, chance is there'll be no 'arps left by the time I gets to the wicket. So I gets to the end o' the line but they got 'arps in good supply and I gets one and the stores bloke puts me name on it; for later, 'e says. So I follows the rest over to a cloud and we 'arp away until stand-easy at 10 'undred before I notices that the other blokes have 'arps that are smaller than mine but make more noise. I asks a bloke 'ow come.

"Oh," 'e says, "these be the new 'arps, the Mark Nines. That un you got's a Mark Two."

Well, I plays along with them the rest of the day, barrin' meals and stand-easies. I finds I don't like 'arpin' much. So next morning at 'ands fall in I decides I'll get out of 'arpin'. I falls in on the starboard side. But it don't work. The Leadin' Angel points to the port side and says, "Them uns there, clean Creator's galley." And he points amidships and says, "Them uns there, clean Creator's cabin." And 'e looks at the rest of us on the starboard side and says, "Rest, 'arpin'."

And that day when I gets to the quartermaster's stores the Stores Leadin' Angel says, "Name?"

"Blobs," I says.

And 'e fishes out that bleedin' Mark Two 'arp again.

Those first few weeks I tries everythin', I'll tell ye. I fell in starboard, port, amidships, wherever – it made no difference; 'arpin', it were, week after week. I complains. The Leadin' Angel says, "Jack, yer just plain destined to 'arp, is all." I tries to get 'im to change me 'arp and 'e says, "Jack, that 'arp ain't wore out. Get 'arpin'!"

So I 'arps. For years, I 'arp. Ten years, 20, 30 –

time don't mean much there – I 'arps with a Mark Two 'arp while all the others is 'arpin' with Mark Nines. Only thing that keeps me from blowin' me lid is the good food and quarters. Roast pork and roast potatoes every day, not just Sundays. But after near 40 years when we comes to re'earsals for the annual Christmas Cantata this year, and I'm put away in the back as usual because of me Mark Two 'arp, I'm blisterin' 'ot. I think in me mick that night, that's enough 'arpin' with a Mark Two 'arp. From now on, no Mark Nine, no 'arpin', and that's final.

So next day when I goes to draw me 'arp and the bloke outs with me Mark Two, I pushes it back and asks for a Mark Nine. 'E says, "No Mark Nines left." I says I been 'arpin' with a Mark Two for near 40 years now and the others all 'ave Mark Nines. 'E says, "That's the Navy way, Jack. Now get 'arpin'!"

So I takes me Mark Two and throws it down and jumps on it. 'E blows a whistle. Shore patrol grabs me quick and stows me in the rattle.

I'm sittin' there next morning when this big Master-at-Arms Angel comes in. 'E looks at me and shakes 'is 'ead and then 'e bawls, "Ordinary Angel Blobs, attenSHUN!"

I attentions.

"Quick march!"

I quick-marches. We quick-marches out of the rattle and down past acres of marble 'alls 'til we comes to a snug little one and we quick-marches in, and there's Creator sittin' by an open port'ole be'ind a desk and we quick-marches right up to the front of the desk.

"'Alt!" shouts the Master-at-Arms Angel.

I 'alts.

"Ordinary Angel Blobs," 'e shouts. "Off 'alo!"

I offs 'alo.

Creator looks up and says, "Ordinary Angel Blobs, you are charged with failin' to 'arp with a Mark Two 'arp when so ordered. Is this charge true?"

"It is, Sir," I says. "But . . . "

"No buts, Ordinary Angel Blobs," 'E says. "Your punishment for this offence is 14 days' 'ell."

Blobs, in his hammock in the Bangor's messdeck, scanned the attentive faces around him. "And that," he said, "14 days' 'ell, since you ask, is 'ow I came to come 'ere."

He had eased on to his back again, his faded eyes staring glumly at the rivet knobs above, when suddenly a big Voice, a mighty Voice, a Voice that filled the head and yet soothed and soothed, sounded as if from far, far above, and also as if from one inch away.

"I didn't really know the whole story, Blobs," the Voice said apologetically.

And through the steel plate above Blobs' head a glowing object materialized in Blobs' hands.

"Wot in 'ell?" he exclaimed, sitting up so fast his hammock spun around three times (but he still didn't fall out). "W'y, it's a bleedin' Mark Nine 'arp!"

"Merry Christmas, Blobs," the big Voice said.

# A PRAIRIE BOY'S CHRISTMAS, 1933

I have to take you in an ambling way to the important instant, for me, of Christmas, 1933. I was 15 then, going to Kelvin Technical High School in Winnipeg, and doing all right in Grade 11 except that I lied a lot, and also stole from time to time; and have always remembered that about myself and in judging others, that when I was poor I lied and stole.

The stealing I can understand better than the lying, but maybe I wouldn't have done either if I had been in a different school than Kelvin. I found it difficult to co-exist with my mainly well-off classmates and still be honest.

My mother did the best she could. It was heroic, even, when you think of it. When we were on relief, my mother and brother and sister and I living in one rented room with a hotplate and two couches that unfolded into beds, she persuaded three bank tellers to become her boarders if she rented an apartment. She found one in the summer of 1932 on Stradbrooke Avenue in the Fort Rouge district.

The tellers paid $35 a month each for room, board and laundry. The three of them slept in one small bedroom. My mother, sister and I slept in the other, smaller yet. My brother slept on the chesterfield in the living room. The seven of us lived on the $105 a month the boarders paid.

From the beginning, there was a slow going into debt; finding it harder and harder to pay the rent and still keep decent food on the table for us and the boarders. I can remember the many nights when mother had to go and talk about the rent with the landlord, who lived in another apartment down the hall in the small two-story building. She would always return pale, but reprieved. He must have been a kind man.

My father wasn't with us. He had gone broke in his own drug store in a small town, Glenboro, and then had worked in the drug department of the Hudson's Bay Company store in Winnipeg before that job folded early in 1931.

He then went north to Flin Flon looking for work. He drove a water wagon for a while, selling it by the pail to housewives on the rocky, hilly streets. He couldn't send much, even when he later got a job at $20 a week in a grocery. A month when he'd send $10 was a big month. There's no bitterness in that. He had his own problems. He would write only rarely but I had the impression that he loved us, which helped. We loved him, too.

When I talked about him to the kids at school, who lived in big and comfortable houses, he became a chemist, engaged in important work in the North. Lying is easy when you get the hang of it. The truth is, in that high school society, I lied to try to make a person of myself.

When I stole, it was for basically the same reason. I competed with my better-off classmates for girls. It is one thing to go to school wearing a pair of $2 pants from an Eaton's sale, a flannelette shirt, and a suit jacket given me by one of the bank tellers when it was too shiny for him to wear to work. It is another to try to dress up for a special occasion.

I had what was called a mackinaw coat. Most of the other kids had good overcoats and wore suits to school that were their own; or decently tailored pants and nice sweaters. I should not have been ashamed of that mackinaw coat, but I was.

Once when I took a girl to a movie in below zero weather I wore only a suit borrowed from one of the tellers. No coat. I wasn't cold, I protested, nearly frozen. I can remember the expostulations of the girl's father, but I contended the coat was just a lot of trouble in the theatre. The money for the show I got by going grocery shopping for my mother, stealing most of the groceries, and keeping the money.

I'm not saying any of this to excuse myself. I am just telling how it was – before, a little later, I was caught stealing, and appeared in juvenile court, and was given such a scare that I never stole again in my life.

I hope the pattern is emerging that led up to that Christmas of 1933. It isn't that my classmates purposely tried to make me feel poor. In fact, I remember some of them with affection; such as one boy who voted for me several times in a class election. I had it won until somebody realized there were more votes

than voters (but I'd only voted once myself, and that
for my opponent).

But when a boy feels inferior, things like clothes
assume a vaster importance than they deserve.

When I dreamed of things I wanted in those days,
I often dreamed of coming to school in a suit so well-
fitting, and well-made, that the others would say,
"Hey, Young ... that's really a neat suit." In a way I
can't properly explain even now, I wanted one good
suit of clothes that would make the others, for a while,
anyway, admit me to their easy circle of weekly allow-
ances, use of the family car, new skates when needed,
and all the rest that gives the affluent that easy bearing
I so admired.

I had a long walk each day to school. It took about
half an hour, walking fast. I would go west through
the snowbanks of Stradbrooke or Wardlaw, modest
enough districts gradually getting better the farther I
went, until I hit Wellington Crescent where the really
rich of Winnipeg lived. There, walking along beside
the high fences with the big houses set away back, I
would begin falling in with the well-dressed.

It would be then that someone might say to me,
"Hey, Young, did you patch that mackinaw yourself?" Or, "Hey, Young, how come one pantleg is
longer than the other?" It was, too, due to an error in
Eaton's alterations department (they didn't spend too
much time on $2 pants on a sale day).

However it happened, by the time I reached Kelvin
each day to mingle with the easy-living kids of River
Heights west of the school, I was feeling humble and

always because of my clothes; something I couldn't shake even by standing higher than all but one of them, exam after exam.

When Christmas approached in 1933, we were badly behind in the rent – and soon to move to a cheaper basement apartment. We had decorated the living room for Christmas by hanging strings of colored paper around the walls, from picture to picture. We were going to buy a tree on Christmas Eve, when the prices would drop to 25 cents. I had been given a dollar to buy presents for Mother, Dad, my sister Dorothy, my brother Bob. It can be done. The Christmas dinner would be good, all right, because that was part of what the boarders paid for.

School was out for the holidays and I was home alone on one afternoon. I remember that important instant of Christmas, 1933, as if I were there again; 15 years old, a voracious reader, a fair skater on the outdoor rinks, and happy, really, that school was out and I could be myself among my own kind until the holidays were over.

I had done some ironing that day for my mother, putting sheets and other flat goods through the big mangle in the block's basement, and had carried it up to the kitchen. When I was there, the doorbell rang.

I walked through the small dining room. The hall was dim, it was always dim, and when I opened the door a man was standing there with a box. It was addressed to me. It didn't have any Christmas wrapping on it, no label saying it wasn't to be opened until Christmas.

I didn't know that in one of my mother's letters to my father, outlining our difficulties, she had mentioned, "Scott badly needs a suit."

I took the box and opened it on the dining room table, and lifted out the suit my father had sent. It was my first new suit, ever. Long after, my father told me that in his troubled existence, he had become obsessed with the idea that even if he couldn't do much, he should buy his eldest son his first new suit.

The material was soft, not scratchy. I couldn't believe how well the jacket fitted me. I put on the pants and they fitted me just as well. I don't know to this day how he got my measurements or whether it was just a guess or whether my mother told him.

I was also given a new white shirt that Christmas, and a tie. On the first day back at school I wore them all; under my mackinaw, but you can't have everything. When I hung my coat in the classroom and walked toward my desk that first morning, Bill Hicks and Fraser Beattie and Dwight Coutts and Norm Toothill all took a look, and then whistled and smiled and grouped around me.

"Hey, Young," they exclaimed, "that's a really neat suit. Where'd you get it?"

I told them my father, the chemist, had sent it to me for Christmas.

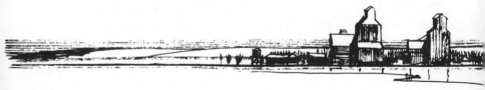

# THE BOY WHO THREW
# A SNOWBALL AT SANTA

nce upon a time away back when most little kids believed in Santa Claus until the first rumors to the contrary hit them around Grade One or so, there lived in a three-bedroom bungalow just inside the city limits a family by the name of Morgan. The parents, Mike and Estelle, had married young and both were 29 and generally happy with one another and the rest of their lot, which, it being 1947, included a 6-percent mortgage, a second-hand car and two kids, Tommy, just past six, and Pearl, nearly three.

In many respects Tommy Morgan was no bargain as a small boy, although it may be that there is no such thing as a bargain in a small boy. He lost a lot of mitts, played his radio under his pillow at night, ate his mother's chocolates, wrote on walls with crayon, lit matches in the garage.

Tommy's father, Mike Morgan, managed a small salesbook factory but, being a former naval officer, often talked to his family as if addressing an assembly of galley slaves. They were used to it and paid little attention. Tommy's mother was really a gem and apparently it wasn't only Tommy who thought that. Tommy's father was always grumbling about not being able to get through the crowd to her at parties.

This Christmas time there was naturally a lot of talk about Santa Claus. Tommy was excited enough about Christmas anyway that he didn't notice how heavy-handed the talk was. When his father imitated Santa Claus's ho-ho-ho-ho laugh until his mother told him to shut up, Tommy took no undue offence. He also laughed as hard as his parents when Pearl, asked to set forth her plans for Christmas day, said that she would get up and "get my new dollies out of the Sanity Closet. Wherever that is."

One night at dinner, Tommy said excitedly that Santa Claus was going to be at school tomorrow, December 23, the last day of school.

"Santa Claus, eh?" asked his father. "Ho-ho-ho-ho!"

Tommy went to his room a little later and jumped on his bed until they yelled for him to stop. Then he went to sleep, thinking warm thoughts about the list he'd given Santa Claus.

At school the next morning when the buzzer rang for recess, Miss Dangerfield stemmed the stampede of Grade Ones, including Tommy. "Santa Claus will be here in only 15 minutes!" she said, smiling at them, slightly flushed herself. "Play nicely until then. And don't get all over snow because after Santa gives you candy outside he's coming to the auditorium and you can all go up and tell him what you want for Christmas." She paused. "All right, dismissed!"

The children got on their heavy coats and boots and ran through the halls filled with excited kids. Outside they separated into groups. Tommy stayed with the Grade One group for a while, and took part in the big talk about Santa Claus, but eventually wandered over to a group of bigger kids.

One, Goofy Garfield, said, "I suppose you're waiting for Santa Claus, eh, kid?"

"So are you," Tommy said shrewdly.

"You know who Santa Claus is?" Goofy asked.

"Santa Claus is Santa Claus," Tommy said.

"Santa Claus is Mr. Grubb," said Goofy.

Mr. Grubb was the school janitor.

"No wonder they call you Goofy Garfield," Tommy said.

Some of the other boys laughed. Goofy Garfield pushed Tommy into the snow and this made Tommy mad. He fought like a wiry, pug-nosed little tiger, and caught Goofy a couple of good ones here and there.

"All right!" said Goofy, sitting on top of Tommy. "He *is* Mr. Grubb!"

When Goofy let him up, Tommy noticed that all the teachers standing on the school steps were looking his way. These included the principal, Miss Staynor, a skinny woman with a fur coat and rusty-red hair tucked into a kerchief. She didn't ever cause anybody much trouble. The kids and their fathers and mothers, some of whom, like Tommy's father, had been taught by her at this same school, all called her Red. She had been there practically forever.

"I think those big boys must be teasing Tommy about Santa Claus," Miss Dangerfield said uneasily. "I heard something the Garfield boy said . . . "

Miss Staynor looked but by that time Tommy was up and had finished brushing himself off.

"Everything seems to be all right now," she said to Miss Dangerfield. "They're just talking."

Out in the schoolyard Tommy was saying, "How could Mr. Grubb be Santa Claus and be janitor of the school at the same time? He couldn't."

"He can be Santa Claus," Goofy Garfield said, "because he just went out about an hour ago and got a Santa Claus suit and a truck and in a little while they'll drive up here and he'll pretend he's Santa Claus and when he's finished he'll take the suit back where he got it and then he'll be Mr. Grubb again. Like every year."

"You're nuts," Tommy said in disgust.

He headed toward his own class but what Goofy Garfield had said bothered him. In a few minutes he went back. "Hey, Goofy," he said scornfully, "how can Mr. Grubb be downtown in the department store being Santa Claus every day and be janitor at the same time?" Another boy, who hadn't heard the earlier ruckus, spoke up. "You been telling this kid that Mr. Grubb is Santa Claus?"

"Yes, he has," Tommy said.

The other boy knocked Goofy down and stuffed snow in his face. Goofy got very mad and yelled to Tommy, "There are dozens of them, just fat guys who pretend to be Santa Claus!"

"But then where is the real Santa Claus?" Tommy asked still another boy, a friend of Goofy's, while Goofy and the first boy rolled in the snow again.

"There isn't any Santa Claus, you sap," the boy said. "It's just crap they feed you kids!"

"Baloney!" Tommy said. "You're goofy, too!"

Then they heard a horn blowing steadily down the street a way. People with shopping bags and parcels stopped on the sidewalk to watch the fun. Little girls shrieked and little boys yelled, and the bigger kids smirked at each other. Some of the teachers smirked, too, standing in the doorway of the red-brick three-story school with Christmas cutouts pasted in the windows. The truck bumped across the sidewalk and rolled to a stop in the schoolyard and all of a sudden the big laughing man in the back, with his ho-ho-ho-ho laugh, looked very phony to Tommy. He crowded a little closer with all the rest of the kids, and looked up at the red-faced Santa Claus and knew that he was Mr. Grubb.

He looked around once to see if Mr. Grubb, in his own clothes, was anywhere in sight. He wasn't. That was enough. Tommy caught a bag of candy and pea nuts Mr. Grubb tossed to him, but there was a queer kind of turmoil in his mind, a choked-up dismay, and he tucked the bag into his pocket and picked up a snowball. Tommy had a pretty good wing, his dad said, for a kid. The snowball caught Mr. Grubb square on his rented whiskers.

Tommy was sorry right away, mainly because he knew it was going to get him into trouble. He suddenly wasn't mad at anybody, Goofy Garfield or Mr. Grubb or his parents or the rest of the world, for stringing him along, or anybody at all. He just wished

he hadn't done it
because it scared him to hear
the sudden groan of horror from
all the little boys and girls and
the exclamations from the people who had been standing on the sidewalk with such fond reflective faces
watching the arrival of the Santa Claus *they* all knew
was Mr. Grubb.

Mr. Grubb stopped his ho-ho-ho-ho-ing.

Tommy saw Miss Dangerfield running for him
across the snow. "Tommy," she called out as she got
close. "Oh ... Tommy!"

She took his hand. He was confused by all this.
She was pulling him toward the school, telling the
other children to stay where they were. At the bottom
of the steps she paused.

"It was those bigger boys, Miss Staynor," she
said. "I saw them teasing Tommy and pointing to, ah,
Santa Claus, and I think they – they told him ... "

Tommy watched Miss Staynor.

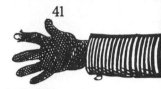

"Come inside, into my office, Tommy," she said.

She took his hand from Miss Dangerfield, and called out, "Go on with everything! You, too, Santa Claus!" Then she opened the school door and the two of them went in.

It was the first time Tommy had been in the principal's office. To hear the other kids talk about being sent to the principal, it was full of straps and other instruments of torture. But it was just a small room crowded with a desk and filing cabinets. Miss Staynor undid the knot on her kerchief and stared at Tommy, fiddling with things on her desk, and then looked out the window. Tommy was sitting in an apprehensive daze, watching her, when the phone rang. When she picked it up he could hear his father's voice, really mad.

Miss Staynor listened and said, "That's what happened, Michael. But I would appreciate it if you would give me a little time ... "

She listened again. "I don't think you should be that hard about it, Michael. This is a case for understanding ... " The voice on the other end of the phone sounded even angrier.

Miss Staynor hung up in the middle of that outburst.

"Come with me, Tommy," she said. "I want to talk to you."

They went downstairs, listening to the party uproar sounding from the school auditorium. Tommy walked like a prisoner with his guard to Miss Staynor's car. They drove through the snowy streets, past the decorated shops and throngs of shoppers, to her apartment building.

On the way upstairs Tommy asked timidly, "What are you going to do, Miss Staynor?"

"I'm going to try to explain to you about Santa Claus," she said. "Your father was going to barge over to the school and get you and I didn't figure I'd have the time, there."

Miss Staynor took Tommy through her apartment, which seemed to him to be a nice place although very clean and unmussed. For the next half-hour Tommy listened attentively. He understood little of what she said. Some words and phrases entered his mind with brief ripples of understanding, like stones dropping into water, but the overall effect was that Miss Staynor wasn't mad at him. For the life of him, he couldn't figure out why. Finally she said, "Do you understand, now, why the symbol shouldn't be ridiculed, even if it is someone you know?"

"Yes," he said, understanding nothing.

"I'll tell Mr. Grubb you're sorry and I'll phone your father and tell him that you've been punished enough by missing the school party. Is that all right?"

"Sure. Thanks," said Tommy.

Tommy walked home. His father was waiting in the living room.

Pearl had brought in her own little wicker chair, to watch. "You're going to get a spanking," she confided

to Tommy.

"Shut up or you'll get one, too," said their father.

"I never threw no snow in no Sanity Closet!" she complained indignantly.

"Come here, you little assassin," Tommy's father said to him. "And don't give me that line like Old Red when she phoned here a few minutes ago and said you've suffered enough, you poor little thing, and you're sorry and now you understand and all that guff."

"She thought you'd come barging over to the school and get me, that's why we got out of there so fast," Tommy said.

"I did but you'd gone, so I just barged home figuring you'd be here hiding behind your mother." He leaned forward with his elbows on his knees and barked at Tommy, earnestly, "Why the heck did you do a bad thing like that?"

Tommy's mother was hovering in the kitchen doorway, looking as if she were enduring thumbscrews, or the rack.

Thinking he saw a small opening, Tommy jumped in. "Miss Staynor said you were really bad yourself in school," he offered.

When his mother giggled behind him he was emboldened to just open his mind to that half-hour in the apartment and just let 'er fly. "She said I shouldn't make you mad because you had a bad temper and in some ways were the worst student she ever handled."

"Yeah, yeah," Tommy's father said hurriedly. "She did, eh? Never mind that, how about you?"

Tommy told about waiting for Santa Claus and about the exchanges with Goofy Garfield.

"That little jerk," said Tommy's father.

Then Tommy told about suddenly realizing it was Mr. Grubb, and throwing the snowball.

"How did Mr. Grubb get in . . . " began Pearl.

"Pearl!" said her mother. "Go to your room." Pearl went.

"Why'd you do that?" Mike asked Tommy.

"Can't you see?" Estelle said, when Pearl was out of earshot. "He was so upset psychologically from realizing that we'd been lying to him about Santa Claus . . . "

Mike roared, "Let *him* answer!"

"I was so upset sike ... sike ... ," said Tommy.

"Psychologically," sighed Mike.

"From realizing you'd been lying to me about Santa Claus ... " Tommy said.

"Oh, migosh," said Mike.

"Anyway," Tommy said, "it seems there really is a Santa Claus. A spirit, or something. Guys who dress up like that are just so kids can understand, because they can't understand anything they can't see, so they have guys dressed up, see?

"Anyway, she took me through this place of hers, it's a little place, and she said if any Santa Claus came into her life she wouldn't ask who he was or anything else but she'd be grateful for him ho-ho-ho-ho-ing and making a little noise around her place for a change. She's got a chicken all for herself, and she says it'll take her a week to eat the damn thing."

"Tommy!" said Estelle.

"Well, that's what she said."

"The damn thing?"

"It was sort of under her breath."

Estelle and Mike exchanged looks again.

"Well, what else?" Mike asked.

"Beside her bed she's got a flashlight and a box of Kleenex and some asthma powder and some sleeping pills, and she said that's what old women like her go to bed with at night. She showed me a box of cigarets in the living room and said she bought them last year in case anybody came at Christmas but nobody came. Anyway, she says I got no business throwing snowballs at Santa Claus."

There was silence for a couple of minutes. Estelle and Mike looked at each other two or three times without speaking and then Mike said, "You're finished until after the holidays, eh – don't have to go back to school?"

"Yep."

"Want to go sliding this afternoon?"

"Sure would! You coming?"

Mike shook his head. "Get some of the kids. But don't say anything about what Miss Staynor told you. Now I'm telling you I'll beat the can off you if you do."

"Okay," Tommy said.

His mother then made him some toast and heated soup and sat Tommy at the kitchen table, while Tommy's father mixed two drinks very fast. On his way past Tommy with the drinks he reached out and jiggled Tommy's elbow, causing him to spill some soup, and grinned back from the doorway.

From the kitchen Tommy listened to their conversation.

"Makes you think a little, eh, what Tommy said about the old girl?" Mike said.

"Mm-hmmm."

"Can't you say anything but grunt?"

"That's not a grunt, it's a murmur."

Tommy was going slow with his soup. He liked overhearing things.

"Damn shame, in a way," Mike said. "I mean, I never really thought about her before, having feelings like that."

"You wouldn't," Estelle sniffed.

"Well, you didn't either."

"I did in a way."

"Baloney!"

There was a silence. About five minutes later Tommy heard his father say, somewhat self-consciously, "She went to a lot of trouble to try to shield little Dillinger out there. Some teachers I've known would have whaled hell out of him and sent a note home suggesting we do the same. I suppose Little Big-Ears is listening to all this."

Little Big-Ears had been. But now he was finished his lunch. He felt vaguely satisfied while he got on his snowboots and heavy jacket and went out to get his sleigh.

So that was the last Tommy heard of that conversation. But on Christmas morning, after the presents had been opened and breakfast eaten and the lovely turkey aroma began sifting through the house to be ready for mid-afternoon dinner with the relatives (it was Mike and Estelle's turn to have the relatives), Mike got the car out and kissed Estelle good-bye and jerked his head at Tommy and Pearl. They got in the car.

It was about noon when they got to Miss Staynor's and tapped on the door. They heard slippers coming. The door was opened by Miss Staynor, holding her spectacles in one hand, dressed in a frilly dark green housecoat that matched a ribbon in her rusty hair.

"Merry Christmas!" said the Morgans in a ragged

chorus.

"Merry Christmas," replied Miss Staynor doubtfully. "Come in."

The little living room had a few Christmas cards on the mantel and a book lying open in a big chair which obviously had been used infinitely more than any of the other chairs. As they entered, Miss Staynor turned and faced the elder Morgan squarely. "What exactly does this mean, Michael?" she asked.

The two younger Morgans were rather proud of the way the old man rose to the situation. He stepped forward and put an arm around Miss Staynor's shoulders and gave her a good squeeze. "Red," he said, "all it means is we'd like you to come to our house for dinner."

She thought it over for a moment, a number of emotions crossing her face, among them pride.

"That way you wouldn't have to eat that damn chicken all by yourself," added Tommy, feeling that maybe an extra push would help.

But Pearl was the one who sealed it. Possibly sensing the need for light conversation at that instant, she burst out the glad news, "It's really Santa Claus, you know, not Sanity Closet! Closets got nothing to do with it at all!"

"She still thinks – well, you know," said the boy who had thrown the snowball at Santa Claus.

# CHEZ CLAUS

eez, I've said it before and I'll say it again – I wish you'd wait until I get the reindeer put away before you start reading the help wanted ads to me."

"Here's one for masseurs. If those young topless broads can make a living rubbing people's backs, think of the effect those whiskers of yours would have on women."

"I tell you I need some time off!"

"Time off! Time off! From that one-day-a-year job of yours? You come back here so pooped I'm starting to wonder how many stockings you looked after, and how many pantyhoses."

"You try driving a sleigh 20,000 miles in one night through all those TV aerials, you'd be cross-eyed, too ... Where's the opener?"

"What opener? Hey, listen to this ... "

"THE OPENER I ALWAYS USE TO OPEN MY COLD BEER WITH WHEN I GET HOME EVERY YEAR AFTER BRINGING JOY TO THE WORLD! THAT'S WHAT OPENER!"

"Oh, *that* opener. I think the elves have got it out at the plant."

"I hate those office parties. Would it be asking too much for you to get it for me?"

"Yes, it would. There's another in the drawer ... But this ad spells Y-O-U. Listen. 'Waiter. Must have pleasant personality and be fully familiar with liquor.' You could always fake the personality bit. With your practice."

"Why don't I just go on the pogey?"

"With our monthly payments – are you out of your mind?"

"Well, dammit, I want something with some dignity."

"Why don't you be a bagman for the Tories – then you could talk only to the Premier, who talks only to God. And that in code, so that not even He knows where the money comes from."

"I tried them once. As soon as they saw my bag, they all fainted. You should have heard them, when they came in. A bagman with an actual bag, they kept yelling. When I got sore they told me I'd better blow or they'd find out where I lived and expropriate the land for a new city. I sometimes wish they would. I could do without this business."

"Then what would all those itsy-bitsy starry-eyed monsters do on Christmas morning?"

"Beat hell out of their parents, I suppose. Are there any peanuts left?"

"You took 'em all with you."

(Moodily) "So I did. I'm all heart."

(Sneering) "Is that what it is? I thought it was the Labatt's balloon you had in there."

"That isn't the way you talked before we got married."

"Damn tootin' it isn't, you fraud. When you patted me on the behind that time outside Eaton's I thought you just wore that red suit for a sideline. Of all the jerk Santa Clauses in the world, I have to pick the real one."

"But it's not all bad, is it?"

"That's not fair. Leave bed out of this."

"Some kid left out some cookies and a bottle of Asti Gancia Spumante."

"You always do this to me when I'm trying to get you a job! Listen ... 'Houseman in Forest Hill' ... "

"Don't try to distract me."

"But why aren't you hungry? Don't you want to eat first?"

"I picked up some oven-ready lobsters. Turn the oven on to 400 and when we're ready, it'll be. Here's your Spumante ... "

"Mmmmmm. The bubbles always get in my nose ... I think. Either that or it's your beard."

"I'll get the door. You get the drapes."

(Giggle) "I won't be able to see to read the help wanteds."

(Chuckle) "No kidding."

# A NIGHT AFTER CHRISTMAS

omewhere I have a snapshot, if I can ever find it, of myself in a toy tin hat carving the turkey at Christmas in 1942. To get the atmosphere think first of blackouts and uniforms and full pubs at night – London in wartime. Many well-off people had moved from their luxurious flats to leave the bombs behind for the safer countryside a couple of years earlier. Some friends of mine had one of those flats in a block called Fursecroft, which also housed the Czech refugee government of the time. My friends' flat had a floating population of dedicated correspondents who were also resolute pub-crawlers. If I could find the snapshot I could verify my memory of who was at that Christmas dinner, but most of us were with The Canadian Press: choose five or six from among Louis Hunter, Alan Randal, Doug Amaron, Ross Munro, William Stewart, Foster Barclay, Ernie Burritt, Allan Nickleson. Most of their bylines, along with mine, were in Canadian newspapers every day at the time on stories that were datelined LONDON (CP) or SOMEWHERE IN ENGLAND (CP).

Louis was going with the Canadian nurse he was soon to marry, named Trennie. Ernie was going with a capricious English girl named Anne who was still car-

rying a torch for a Polish flyer with whom she had
lived for a while, near Torquay, before he was killed in
action. Alan we called Kayo (and still do). Foster must
have had a girl (he always did). Al Nickleson then was
not going with Georgina, demonstrating – she lived
near by – that even ultimately wise men are sometimes
slow to act (they later married). My own unstated
admiration was for an Australian girl named Dulcie,
whom I found out later felt warmly about me as well,
but we did nothing about it. I was married, my wife in
Canada, and Dulcie also was married, to a trombone
player in Geraldo's Band, a big one of the time. At
parties we sat together a lot and talked, but nothing
more.

Many of those were at that Christmas dinner,
along with at least one RCAF public relations officer,
Bob Forster, and a woman I'll call Mary. She tended
one section of the bar at a pub just off Fleet Street.
Sometimes Mary's section was called the Canadian
bar, to distinguish it from the more thickly populated
Australian bar in the same pub. Mostly it is Mary I
think about when I remember that Christmas dinner.
Not for something that happened then, but for something that happened later.

Mary tended to mother us through the long even-
ings we spent at her counter. We were mostly in our
twenties, she in her early forties. She had a matronly
look and figure, and wore dentures. None of us lusted
after her and, in truth, it probably did not occur to us
that anyone would again. (We were young enough to
make such empirical, unconscious judgements.)

One night in that pub over a few drinks, and under the influence of a strolling fiddler who had come in through the blackout curtains to play and sing I'm Dreaming of a White Christmas, we began talking about what we would do at Christmas. Was there any way, by pooling our food rations, that we could buy a turkey? Ernie Burritt was the key. He was a shrewd tipper and he never neglected butchers. He thought he could get a turkey.

"If you get one," said Mary, "I'll fix it for you."

Ernie got the turkey, with Foster's assistance. At Short's bar on High Holborn in those days, the regulars were allowed to buy Scotch whisky, which was scarce elsewhere. We were regulars, as were many RCAF men from nearby headquarters at Lincoln's Inn Fields. We amassed the appropriate amount of whisky, and scoured our usual sources for tall bottles of beer, both dark and light, to stockpile for Christmas Day.

On Christmas Day, when Mary arrived at Fursecroft to cook the turkey, for some reason I spent a lot of time with her in the kitchen, talking. The others straggled in. We poured drinks, got the fireplace going (coal was short, but the Fursecroft guerrillas had some). I can't remember the exact turn of the conversation that brought Mary and me around to talking about children. She said she had always wanted a child, but now was unlikely to have one. I am afraid I was not able to offer her much encouragement, let alone help, but later I thought of it again as I saw how she fussed over us all and made it a Christmas dinner

to remember even though some were dreaming of
Christmases far away. Too bad, I thought, that Mary
never had a family to do all these things for.

It was a year and a half later before I thought of it
again. I had returned to Canada briefly and was back
in England in the Navy. I went into the pub where
Mary had worked. She was not there. I asked where
she was. There was a mixture of indignation and
amusement in what my friends told me. Most of the

Australian air force men who went into that pub tried, from time to time, to get in bed with the dark-eyed, pretty woman who looked after the Australian part of the bar. But one night a man who felt he couldn't compete, maybe, in that league wandered across to the bar where Mary was. I don't know if it happened that night, or soon after, but it happened. "He got Mary pregnant and never came back," I was told. "Worried? If she was, she never let on. She had the baby. Funny thing is, she's happy as hell about it."

Funny thing, indeed. I haven't seen her since but can still picture and hear her in the kitchen at Fursecroft that Christmas of 1942, tall, skinny legs, big-busted torso, telling me she had always wanted a child.

# THE SAMARITAN

If anything the bar was quieter than usual about suppertime on the night before last. It was as if Christmas Eve had come a day early this year. People who had homes had gone to them. The customers were all men and they sat and drank silently as if their talking had been done.

They lifted their eyes when this guy came in from the street, carrying an armful of parcels. He wore a white shirt and a bow-tie and was drunk. When he gave a hoist to the parcels to get them up on the bar, a man nearby made a quick move to keep one of the packages out of a wet spot, but wasn't in time.

Some parcels had been Christmas-wrapped in stores, but a child's pink flannelette nightgown spilled out of one plastic bag and from another dribbled the cord and red wooden knob of maybe a pull-toy.

The bartender wiped the counter in front of the man and stacked the parcels neatly in a dry spot and said, "Shopping late, eh, Mr. Rogers?"

"Make it a double, Charlie," the man said. "No hurry. Any time in the next 10 seconds will do fine." He did his own laughing. Nobody else along the bar smiled but guys were watching him directly, or in the mirror. When he glanced around most of them

dropped their eyes to their drinks or stared at their own eyes in the mirror.

He drank that double and when he was on the last drops, the bartender said, "Want me to call you a cab, Mr. Rogers?"

"Not yet. Same again."

The bartender didn't move right away. The man was fishing around in his money on the bar. He dropped a dime and when he scrambled for it under his stool, he fell to his knees and elbows on the floor and toppled over.

On the bartender's way along the bar everybody was watching, but the privacy that brings people alone to bars was in effect among them: an older man neatly dressed, a black young man wearing a toque, a guy in a

coat with a crest that said Toronto Harbour Police 1972, a fat man in a frayed suit, and a young man who was completely bald and whose beer was empty.

"Want another?" the bartender said to him. The bald young man said yes. Charlie got the beer. Down the bar, Mr. Rogers was calling for some action. The fat man said in a low voice to the bartender, "Know him?"

Charlie: "Salesman or something. Works around here."

"Is he like this all the time?"

"He doesn't usually have the parcels." Then he shrugged. "Ah-h-h-h, he's usually okay. A beer or two, then off home."

The bartender drew a couple more beers, for others. Mr. Rogers was annoyed. "Are you refusing to serve me?" he called.

The bartender went back. His face was closed. He stood in front of Mr. Rogers and said, "Your kids are probably waiting to see what kind of parcels you're bringing home. I know how kids are." A voice said, "He's just trying to help you, man." Several others nodded.

Things got worse from there. Maybe a guy in a bar is not used to being with other drinkers and facing obvious disapproval. That figured: it rarely happens. Now it was a battle of wills and the guy with the parcels had all the ammunition.

"I want to show you gentlemen," he said, dwelling on the word gentlemen, "what I got for my little girl." A torn bag fell to the floor and he took a doll out of a box. He tipped it and it made a crying sound. There wasn't another sound in the bar. "Now for the big trick," he said.

He took a tiny bottle from the box and removed its rubber nipple and picked up the half-bottle of beer in front of the man next to him. He poured beer into the doll's bottle, slopping it a little. The man next to him grabbed the little bottle and with a fierce gesture grabbed the doll, too. "You'll ruin it, you durn fool," he growled.

Mr. Rogers laughed. The man next to him drained the beer from the little bottle, wiped it, got the paper off the floor, smoothed it out, and laid the doll and bottle back in the box.

"Charlie!" Mr. Rogers demanded.

"No more for you, Mr. Rogers," Charlie said quietly. "That's definite."

The well-dressed older man tried to talk quietly about how he'd be better if he went home. Several others tried. Nothing worked. Mr. Rogers gripped the bar and stared straight ahead, white with anger, his mouth working.

Nothing more happened for a minute or two. Then the bald young man, who had been silent but watchful, certainly causing no trouble, got up from his end of the bar and walked along to Mr. Rogers and said, "I don't blame ya, Mac! These preachers make me sick!"

Now the two of them yelled at the bartender. They screamed profanity. The other customers stared, startled, and then hunched closer over their drinks, their shoulders seeming to shrink, as Charlie came out from behind the bar and tried to propel the two of them toward the door. The bald young man grabbed a stool and Mr. Rogers grabbed the cigarette machine and both hung on.

That lasted a few seconds until the young man suddenly relaxed his grip and said, "All right, Mac, let's get outta here. Find a better dump. Don't hafta take this kinda crap."

Mr. Rogers glared around, losing his balance, grabbing the cigarette machine again to steady himself.

"I'll help ya with the parcels," the young man said.

He loaded a few parcels on Mr. Rogers and took

most of them himself. Outside they could be seen through the window, coats open, reeling to the curb, the bald young man's arm up to get a passing cab. It pulled over. They piled the parcels in the front seat and got in the back. The taxi disappeared and there was a long, sad silence in the bar.

Most of them were still there an hour later, when the bald young man came back, in another taxi. He walked steadily along the bar, hung up his topcoat, and sat where he had been before. The bartender approached warily.

"He lives away out," the bald young man said. "One of the parcels had a bill in it with the address. I had to carry him in. But the kids were downstairs watching TV, his wife said."

All the men in the bar were listening and there was a dawning look of delight in some of their eyes. "How's about a cold one?" the bald young man said.

When he got it, he poured it carefully. When the glass was full he raised it and sipped. Suddenly all the men along the bar wanted to look at him. They craned this way and that to see around their neighbors, or looked into the bar mirror to catch his eyes, and when they did they winked or nodded and smiled.

# GLAD TIDINGS FROM THE
# PAPER BOY

Once, there was a boy of 13 who had The Globe and Mail paper route on Brookdale Avenue in North Toronto, between Yonge Street and Avenue Road. He was a tall and thin boy who did not like getting up at six every morning, any more than you would, madam. But his paper route brought him about $8 a week, and that he did like.

And also once he was up and out there were certain other things that he liked. Often the only people he saw in the mornings were other paper boys, and although they did not know one another at all they sometimes whistled and waved from one street to another across an empty stretch of the city. It is always good to know that one is not alone.

Globe and Mail boys work on Christmas mornings, too, you know. Many of them are still young enough that they pass by the silent Christmas trees on their way out and look at the piles of parcels, but then press on hoping that when they get home there will be others up. That was the way it was with this one, back there around the Christmas of 1958.

It was odd that morning, he told me later. All the sights and sounds with which he had become quite familiar had been suspended. There was one man on Brookdale who always was up in the winter shovelling his driveway. "It would be awfully still some mornings and I could hear him more than a block away. Scrape, swish, scrape, swish. Sometimes he would say hello to me, but sometimes he would just keep his head down while I passed."

On this Christmas morning the house of the inveterate snow shoveller was quiet and still. A day off.

In another house there was always a girl up practising piano. The piano was in the living room. The windows looked out on a verandah the width of the house. She would have one light on above the piano by her metronome. "She must have known sometimes that I was there, because I would come up on the verandah to drop the paper – although I never threw it against the door or anything like I sometimes did at other houses. I would glance in and she would be sitting there wrapped up in what she was doing. I would just glance. I wouldn't stand there looking. But she never once looked up."

On this Christmas morning that house was quiet, too. No light on above the piano. No girl.

"I used to like looking in at the Christmas trees," the paper boy said. "All the week before Christmas, every morning there would be new ones, big or small, each one changing as more presents or decorations were added. I liked the ones where the lights had been left on all night."

It was through one of those front windows, on that Christmas morning, that he saw the little boy. The

tree lights were on, and by their glow he could see a
kid in sleepers hunkered down on his haunches the
way children can do it, his hands on his knees. The
little boy was alone in the sleeping house, just looking,
and his eyes could be seen, with a look in them of
wonder and excitement.

He didn't move when the paper boy came up on
the verandah and saw him, and dropped the paper
quietly at the door.

Then the paper boy, long and thin, his toque
pulled low over his ears, moved silently to the front
corner of the house – as close as he could get to the
little boy and still be out of sight.

"Ho! Ho! Ho!" the paper boy laughed, as loudly
as he could. "Ho! Ho! Ho! Ho!"

The little boy inside ran to the front window and
stared into the sky, his eyes bigger than ever.

The paper boy tiptoed away a minute later and
finished his deliveries.

# THE RAGTIME SHOES

he best way to polish off Christmas Eve is with a good mystery story, and by a remarkable coincidence I have one here. A friend of mine brought it in, tossed it on my desk, and said, "One of my kids has been reading your stuff and thinks it is a good racket, so he started to write stories." The author's name is Andy Scott. He is 10. His story follows, with my comments in brackets. It is entitled,

### THE RAGTIME SHOES

*(It is said that the true test of a mystery story is the title. If the author has made even the title so mysterious that you don't have the slightest inkling of what the story is about, it is a fine augury. As it happens, I have read the story and I still don't understand the title. This makes the author's future even brighter. However, on with the story.)*

In the year of 1854 there was a group of bad bandits in the west. *(All the good bandits must have been in the east that year.)*

The group took turns each week to rob and make things worse. This time it was Harry and Reshaws turn to do the dirty work. Many a man heard of these two certain people and there instinct told them that they should stay as far away from them as posible.

They were both wanted in San Francisco for killing the sherriff of the town. One thing people did not no about them. That was where there hideout was and another thing people did not no about them was what made them tick. Harry was known for his good fist fighting and Reshaw was known for his good gun hand. They could use whatever plan for the crimes, in the club, that they wanted.

RESHAW

This week they were told to hold up the bank and send all the money to their top boss in San Francisco and split it up.

It was a day before the crime when they were talking about there plan at the back of an old salloon bar.

They were drinking water like wiskey. *(The author later edited this to read, wiskey like water, thus eliminating a laugh. This must never be done in editing, so I have restored the original.)*

This was there plan that they had decided. When they send the money to there top boss they were to sent it in a shoe because the boss always handled his parsels since they were usely for him and the letters were for his wife. And the shoe was to be in a parsel.

The night of the crime was dark and it was raining.
There was lightning to. Then the bank was just about
to close when they came in. Then Harry said,
"Reach," and they cleaned out the bank which happened to have a lot of money in it. *(But not, one hopes,
more money than would fit in a shoe.)*

"Boy that was sure a good cleanout," said Harry.
"Now to send it to the boss."

That night they went to a hotel. Harry said his
name was George Clinton and Reshaw said his name
was Peter Grant. They did this because they did not
want to arousse any suspision. They had a good night's
sleep and got up the next morning. They had there
grub and were going to sent the money to there boss
now. So that's what they did.

At the same time the banker that had been robbed
last night by Harry and Reshaw was in the sherriff's
office telling about all that happened that night. *(He
had a previous engagement, so couldn't see the sherriff
earlier.)* When he told them the story, the sherriff
spoke up. "Are you sure this isn't a dream you had last
night? It can happen you no."

"I'm sure," the banker said. "OK then," said the
sherriff. "We'll sent a couple of men out to see if they
can grab them or any evedinse."

They went over to the bank and looked around for
some evidense. *(The author already has grasped one
basic of newspaper writing – when in doubt about a spell-
ing, employ the law of averages.)*

They saw a cigar but. Then the sherriff turned his
head to the banker and asked, "Is this your cigar or

was it here before last night?"

The banker nodded his head and said, "No, I can't say there was." *(A banker to the end, he couldn't say yes even while nodding his head.)*

"Well, thanks," said the sherriff, wile walking out of the bank.

There wasn't much to go on but they went to a store that sold cigars. They asked the man at the counter what kind of a cigar this was.

Then the old man at the counter spoke up. "Well, anybody noes that," he said. "It's a cornella."

"Well, I'll be," said the sherriff. "Evidense all ready."

*(I admit there's a sort of Ginger Coffey kind of an ending to that. However, I think if you sit back and light up a cornella and think about it for a wile, sooner or later your feet will hit the floor and you'll say, "Well, I'll be." Just like the sherriff. If not louder. And a Merry Christmas to you, too.)*

# HOME FOR CHRISTMAS

race Magee had been working like a dog at the housework, which she hated. She got a beer and slouched down in the big chair in the corner by the television set, resting the cold bottle just below her ample breasts. Children had rested there and men too, from time to time, although fewer men lately than once had been the case; that thought crossed her mind without particular emphasis. Three of the children, children no longer, were coming today or tomorrow, they never got too specific. That's why she was cleaning the house. Not that they'd notice. They'd come in with their cases of beer and parcels still to be wrapped and the place would be thunderous with their feet and their voices. She'd lived there 17 years, the house originally built cheap as a chalet, pine and plywood and a big stone fireplace but with none of your traditional farmhouse peace and quiet. "Hey, Amazing!" they'd whoop as they charged in and hugged her, always the same greeting. They never called her Mother or Mom like other people's kids. Expected her to sit up late and drink beer for beer with them because she always had.

The thought had been in her mind from time to time that she'd sell this place, but she hadn't, yet. I'm just a slave to the goddamn past, she thought; each

year cutting two red pines from the grove they'd planted in 1969, one for inside and one for outside. Decorating them with relics that went right back to the first year of her marriage, freezing her hands getting the outside lights up this afternoon before the start of the blizzard that was swirling across the deck right now.

Drinking her beer, her feet resting on the vacuum cleaner she hadn't quite finished with, she looked through the blowing snow at the outside lights and imagined the way they looked from the hill corner. The kids always said it looked nice when they turned that corner half a mile away and could see the lights, even in a storm. She'd turned them on when darkness fell hours ago even though she wasn't really expecting anyone until tomorrow, the 24th, especially as it was near midnight now.

She was taking another swallow from the bottle when she heard a noise outside, footsteps on the stairs leading to the deck.

Then she could see a man approaching the big glass door and standing there peering in. Right away she knew that she didn't know him, but she went to the door when he was raising his hand to knock, and opened it, the snow sifting in.

*And how he was dressed!*

She took it all in at once: a young guy in jeans and loafers, snow halfway up his legs, a tweed jacket over one of those tight shirts that opened right down to his belly button showing a hairy bare chest.

"Come in, come in," she said. "I didn't hear your car drive up."

He stepped inside on the carpet where people generally stopped to take their boots off, or at least wipe them.

"Uh," he said, "Mrs. Magee?"

"Yeah, do I know you?"

"Not really. I'm a friend of Melvin's. Um, we're stuck down the road a bit but I figured this must be the place. It was the only light I could see."

"But where's Melvin, then?" Melvin was her youngest son, 22, who had been working on an oil rig on Ellesmere Island, flying out by way of Edmonton a few days earlier.

The young man looked embarrassed. "Um, he stayed with the car."

"Melvin stayed with the car and you didn't know for sure if this was our place? Oh, of course – you'd just walk along the road and see our name on the mailbox."

"Actually," he said, "I was afraid that if I stuck to the road I might lose sight of your lights. I came across the fields."

"*Across the fields?* In that outfit?"

He nodded.

Telling the story later, it could be kept shorter. It seemed that Melvin had decided to surprise her by coming a day early. He had come by bus from Toronto to Peterborough and had been going to take a taxi from there but had gone to the Red Onion tavern for a drink first and there he'd run into his old school friend who said he'd give him a lift. But before they started out they had a few more drinks. It came out that Melvin had killed a mickey of rum earlier, finishing it off on the bus. So that even before they slid off the road into the ditch by George Wilson's gate, sliding off being made easier because the car had bald tires, no snows, Melvin had passed out and could not be roused. Hence this one's trek for a mile through trees and snowdrifts and fields and up the steep sumach-crowded hill, tough enough to walk through even in summer. He hadn't worn a coat, he said, because he thought it would be just out and back in the warm car.

Grace got out her own small two-door with front-wheel drive. She put on her down parka and Grebs and found an old parka and snowmobile boots for Melvin's friend, whose name was Delamere Jones, a distant relative of some other Joneses around here, and Grace, knowing these roads in winter since Melvin was in kindergarten, drove safely to where Delamere's car was. She could not rouse Melvin, either. Her youngest son for the moment was a big inert lump with a breath like she didn't know what.

"We'd better get him into my car," she said.

Melvin weighed 200 pounds. He was six feet tall. In the blowing snow, Grace dragged from under his armpits and Delamere took the feet. It went all right until they tried to slide him head and shoulders first into the back seat. He was so limp that there was no way they could shove him in. Finally Grace got in, swearing and laughing, and pulled him in after her with Delamere shoving from the foot end. Then Grace climbed over into the driver's seat and drove them home. They couldn't get him up the steps to the main door but there was an old mattress in the basement, which had its own door, so that is where they left him, fully dressed and covered with a duvet that Grace carried down from upstairs, tucking him in and loving her dumb, reckless son, sometimes undisciplined but never before like this.

"You better stay over," she puffed to Delamere, upstairs. And, looking up into his eyes, a young man's eyes, thinking there was a twinkle there now that it was all over, she said, "Jesus, you could of both frozen to death, you in the field and him in the car. Thanks a million."

"No problem," Delamere said earnestly, which broke them both up.

The next morning after Delamere and Melvin had gone to meet a tow truck so that Delamere could get back to his own Christmas somewhere, her second son Garth, short and wiry, at 23 a year older than Melvin, drove up in his elderly Olds Cutlass. He arrived at the door with his arms full of parcels, some others carried by a dark-haired, thin, shy but eager-to-please girl Grace had never seen before. Her name was Teresa and they both put their stuff in Garth's old bedroom, to no surprise from Grace, who had not been aware Garth was bringing a girl. Grace in general thought

Garth was very responsible, the only one of her kids who had actually finished university and was now repaying his student loans.

From when Melvin had wakened in the morning and appeared, a 200-pound wraith, in the kitchen, he was cheerful when someone was talking to him but in repose looked withdrawn. Grace thought about that, wondering why. Not like him at all. She tried to pump him a little but all she got was about his work on the oil rigs and that he'd stayed a few days in Edmonton on the way out. All in all, he appeared none the worse for abusing himself with booze. In that, Grace thought, he took after his father, Milford. Many's the time Milford had drunk the Legion dry and got home okay. Until he took off with rather a nice woman, who deserved better, drink had been his only big fault.

She spent the day stuffing the turkey and letting Garth and Teresa decorate the tree and noticing that they touched each other a lot. Grace liked that. It warmed her heart. She could remember that feeling, being with someone who liked to touch her. Once Garth came out to the kitchen and stood beside her while she was rolling pastry with an empty rum bottle in lieu of a rolling pin, a family tradition which had started once when her rolling pin was lost and Milford had produced the empty, laughing, "We'll never run out of these."

After standing a minute Garth said, "Say, Amazing ... "

"Yeah?"

"Is it against your religion for me and Teresa to

smoke a joint?"

She had not given the subject a second's thought before, but now that she did, she said, "Nope."

"Ever try it yourself?"

"Nope." Still rolling the pastry.

"Want to?"

"Nope." Once or twice she had been offered it, but had concluded she was comfortable with the vices she had and didn't need any new ones. But she didn't say that because it sounded too pat.

But when the stuffed turkey was in the fridge and the mince pies were in the oven and, with Teresa watching closely and asking questions as if Grace was the old professor at keeping men happy, she was starting to mix the meat for the pork pies which, hot, were what they always had on Christmas Eve, she began to worry a little that her oldest, Ralph, 25, hadn't arrived. He just had to drive from Orangeville. Then he did get there just at dark, rolling up in his old red Duster, slewing up the steep driveway, giving her a huge hug at the door. He was short and stocky, built like she was, laughing, telling jokes, turning the music up so loud everybody yelled at him. He didn't have a wife or a girlfriend – maybe a boyfriend, Grace thought, but wasn't sure. It was late in the evening with the fireplace going and the big room warm and noisy and the lights flickering on the Christmas trees both inside and outside that Ralph said he'd been laid off a week ago, the firm he worked for gone broke.

Still, it didn't put a damper on the evening. They played Christmas music. Little Drummer Boy. Good

King Wenceslas. Silent Night. Melvin was quiet for a while, drinking beer slowly, as if he had a bargain with himself about it, and then in one break in the carols he stood up and sang, rather nicely, Away in a Manger and then,

> "We Three Kings of Orient are,
> Trying to light a rubber cigar,
> It was loaded, it exploded,
> Now we're on yonder star."

Everything was going very well, Grace thought. Melvin was his young cheerful self part of the time. Garth was sitting with his hand gently resting on the back of Teresa's neck, a fond place for his hand to be. Ralph had lost his job but you'd never know it. "I'll deal with it in January," he said, when the subject came up, as it did.

Grace also wondered a little about the girlfriend Garth had had for years, almost from high school, continuing in college because the girl, Corinne, had also gone to Waterloo where Garth was; Grace had liked Corinne, but that was life. Garth and Corinne had never touched as much as Garth and Teresa did, that was a fact, and maybe an important one. Time would tell.

Some time after midnight they trailed off to bed, Grace to her own, reading a while, placing her Kleenex handy, thinking of Christmases gone by. And how, although she was not a sentimental sort (she thought), these brief times with her family were, well, part, maybe the most important part, of what she enjoyed about life, these days. Some day she would get an apartment. Maybe one or all would get married or whatever and ask her for Christmas and to bake for families yet unknown, unforeseen, her special Christmas Eve pies. Grandma. It could happen, couldn't it?

That night before she put out her light she got out of bed and stood in her flannelette nightgown before the long mirror door that enclosed her closet. What she saw was a woman with light brown hair and a body going heavy no matter what she did to stop it. Her thighs and legs had always been too big, she thought. But she had been the goal of many a man besides Milford. She had been in love a few lovely times before they married and after he left. And, still, when a man looked at her that way she knew what was happening, to him and sometimes to her. May it never end.

It was in the morning, Christmas morning, that she found out about Melvin. She went into his room to tidy up and make his bed, having done the same for Ralph but not for Garth and Teresa, let them cover their own tracks, and found propped against the lamp on Melvin's night table a color snapshot of a woman in a red dress, a smiling woman lying on a rug with two small children, one on either side. Beside the photo was the last page of a letter which Grace read, she could not help herself. She did not look at the first pages, but this one said:

"I'm still surprised at what happened so quickly. Our time in Edmonton was really a bit of magic – the way you loved me and the way I loved you. I don't know if we can ever surpass that, but it is important that you know I have never been happier. I am going to miss being with you in every way that is possible.

"Till we are close again.

"I love you. Diane."

Grace made Melvin's bed, taking care not to disturb the photo or the letter. Now she understood the bottle of rum, my God, coming home for Christmas but leaving that, the sound of that love, behind. A woman far away and yet she felt a kinship. Judging by the children probably a few years older than Melvin but what did that matter? Grace thought of words of love spoken or written to her, words long since forgotten, or burned, and thought of the longings of love and how they filled a mind.

In the kitchen her three sons and Teresa were getting ready for the presents under the tree by pouring juice, coffee, eating bits of leftover pie, laughing and talking. Grace went directly to put her arm around Melvin and squeezed him, noting his expression, at first startled, then not – perhaps, she thought, he was suddenly aware of where she had just been, straightening his room, and what he had left by his bed that she might have seen. She squeezed him again, hard, and then let him go and stepped away.

"I've gotta put the turkey in," she said. "Otherwise it'll never be done."

# HARK, THE HERALD ANGEL

my fell asleep around midnight because it was past her usual go-to-sleep time. But she kept waking. If she wakened lying on her left side facing the bedside phone, she could also see the red numbers on her clock radio. However, if she wakened lying on her back, she always saw, first thing, the huge water stain on the ceiling above her head. Then, she'd look at the clock. A few years ago, her daughter Aeronwy, having taken some angel dust (by mistake, she claimed, causing Amy to ask what did she think it was, Johnson's Baby Powder?), had gone into one of that drug's specialties, a depressed stupor, and let the bath run over.

In next-day penitence, the kid had proclaimed that she would have the ceiling redone as soon as she was rich and famous. That had not happened yet. So, one way or another, the clock and the ceiling stain kept reminding Amy that this was a hell of a way to spend Christmas Eve, which by now had edged into Christmas morning.

The twice she got up and went into Aeronwy's bedroom, it was more for the exercise than anything else. It wasn't like the years when any time she went into that bedroom at night it was to see if the kid was home yet. Aeronwy was 3,000 miles away and Amy certainly would have been able to stand Christmas Eve by herself, without even a phone call (if that was her fate), have a few drinks alone and read; yep, she could have stood being alone if the telegraph office hadn't phoned with the woman saying, "Telegram for Amy Falkener."

"That's me," Amy said.

"Message reads: 'Please be home all night for phone call. Urgent. Love, Aeronwy.'"

The woman then hesitated and said, "What kind of a name is Aeronwy?"

"Welsh," Amy said. "Her father is Welsh." Yep, Welsh and long gone now, but when Amy had given birth to her only child her husband had wanted that name, the same name as Caitlin and Dylan Thomas's daughter. "Might bring ours luck," he said. "Law of averages."

Not that waiting for the kid, in person or on the phone, was a new experience. When Aeronwy'd been singing around here before she went to try the big leagues, often she went out after for a few beers or whatever with the guys in whichever band she was with. Earlier, at 16, 17, in there, she was supposed to phone if she was going to be late. When Amy was writing for a living, that was okay because she was often up late at her typewriter. But four years ago, her writing simply dried up. Bread-and-butter articles that bought groceries she simply couldn't face any more. Her short stories, once her real talent, suddenly wouldn't come off. She'd had to get a job and she could type, so she was a typist. She still thought about her writing. "The promising young short-story writer, Amy Falkener," she would read on a 15-year-old dust jacket. Or, now, "The once-promising . . ." Anyway, with her job, the always-phone-home rule had gradually fallen into disuse. Their flat, part of a house, was in Scarborough, the only place in Toronto she could find two bedrooms that she could afford, and public transportation stopped at about the same time the kid stopped playing, most gigs. A call at 2 or 3 a.m. didn't bring her home, but did leave Amy groggy when her alarm went off.

This Christmas morning finally around three Amy knew she couldn't get back to sleep. She made tea and determinedly picked up the book she was re-reading, a biography of George Orwell; he had struggled but prevailed.

What could this phone call from Aeronwy be about? If it had just been Merry Christmas and a lament on how broke she was or what her voice teacher had said or thanks for the Christmas money order ($200 U.S. costing $250 Canadian), why specify tonight? Aeronwy usually could cope with whatever came along, but she was also reckless. Amy's night then became like the line that when you're going down for the third time your whole life flashes before your eyes.

In Amy's case it was that part of her life that focused on the kid: the three-year-old in a powder-blue snowsuit walking through a snowy park on a sunny day, never looking where she stepped, her eyes steadily turned upward to the sky. The 10-year-old sweetly singing The Twelve Days of Christmas. The 12-year-old singing her own mildly wicked parody of the same song. Amy getting into her car on many midnights (curfew 11 p.m.) to go looking. Driving to the roller rink – how old was Aeronwy then? Fourteen or 15. Couldn't find her. Asking a girl she knew, "You seen Aeronwy?" The girl looking blank, their union had strict rules. "Oh, I think she's gone home."

When Amy would get home, Aeronwy might even be there. The stories: she'd lost her subway tokens and walked home. She'd had a hamburger with a guy and hadn't noticed the time. She'd left her roller skates in a guy's car and had to get another guy to drive her all the way to Pickering to get them! Once a guy named Earl, driving her home from a gig at a high school, had taken the wrong turn at Highway 401; then it was 4 a.m. and Aeronwy was in the kitchen. Wide-eyed: "The next thing I knew, Mom, I see this sign that says Guelph."

Now, more grown up, there she was in glorious color on the wall; singing into a microphone she held in her hand, a montage of wildly moplike magenta hair, Dracula eye make-up, a black leather bomber jacket over a black leather miniskirt – a rock singer's uniform. Amy thought of the nights when she was still writing and Aeronwy was just starting out and would come home from a gig and get into one of her warm flannelette nightgowns and a comfortable old dressing gown and they'd sit in the dinette and talk.

The first time the kid really stayed out all night without giving notice, Amy had been wakened by some noise and saw that it was 6:58, her alarm about to go off. She got up and walked the few steps out of her bedroom and across the dinette. Aeronwy was standing by the kitchen sink getting a drink of water.

"Hi, what happened?" Amy said.

Aeronwy by then had her first freaky hairdo, bleached and starched to stand up and make her a foot taller. "After the gig it turned out that Dino was there. I hadn't noticed him sitting away at the back out of the lights, but we were sort of glad to see each other and . . ." She shrugged. It was enough. Aeronwy and Dino had once been lovers, very physical, and Amy, physical enough herself, had supposed that this had been (as the English put it), going back for afters.

The kid and Dino had lived together for nearly a year, when she was 18 and Dino 21. At the time Amy's options had been either to put up with it, and keep in touch, or totally lose contact. Amy had put up with it, once even defended it. A woman from work had been on her back about letting her daughter live with a guy. Amy, having had a few drinks, blurted out airily, "Ah, any woman has a right to one real macho Italian in her life." Or Welshman.

Dino's mother, a proper mother, called Amy to wail that she had decided just to pretend that their children were married, until they actually were. To help the illusion along, she'd given them an ornate bedroom suite that took up so much of their tiny apartment's bedroom that the door would only open about a foot. (Later, from Aeronwy: "Dino had to be careful that he didn't think of sex until he was in the bedroom, or he couldn't get through the door.")

Anyway, Dino's mother kept bugging them to get married until eventually, from all the Sunday dinners and home-made wine and whatever, Aeronwy had gone for it. Maybe deep down, Amy thought at the time, she'd had some kind of yearning for a regular day-to-day life with a man in it. Hadn't learned a thing from her own father taking off and leaving the two of them. One night late she had told Amy she and Dino were going to get married on her 19th birthday.

What Amy did then she'd been proud of ever since, like saving somebody's life by sheer will-power just short of them being swept over Niagara Falls. The thing was, she'd known that if she fought she would lose.

"So why?" she said, much more calmly than she felt.

Aeronwy explained Dino's mother's insistence that she couldn't stand to see her son living common-law when all her friends' kids, male or female, were having big weddings with receptions and a live band and people banging their glasses for the happy couple to kiss one another, and all that stuff.

"And Dino wants it, too. Anyway, we decided."

Amy thought it over for a minute or two, then held her flame of anger in tight control to say mildly, "Well, I'm not going to say you shouldn't."

"Well, thanks a lot!" Aeronwy flared.

Amy wanted to scream, "What do you think, I'm going to fall over backwards with sheer joy that you're going to blow everything you always said you wanted just because some hunk with his shirt undone to his navel wants to own you? You with your goddamn line that I always believed, that what you want from life is to be a musician, a singer!"

But what she actually said was, still calmly, "You're 18 now, but a few years from now when maybe you're ready for something big, to go on the road, go somewhere else to work, do you think you'll be able to do it if you're a nice housewife with three little kids?"

"We love each other, Mom."

As it turned out, by the time her 19th birthday came she and Dino weren't even living together. He'd gone back to Mama, taking the bedroom suite, and Amy didn't rub it in when Aeronwy came one day and said, "Mom, can I come back?"

Amy liked the nights a little after that when maybe on a Sunday, just loafing, the kid would tell about how this song or that had gone the night before – some she'd written herself and sometimes could get bands to play. A few times Amy went to her gigs, like the first time she played El Mocambo. To Aeronwy, it was like some others would feel playing Carnegie Hall . . .

Then there was the time the kid was trying to explain her particular kind of music to the woman next door who had attempted to show how with it she was by interrupting, "You mean, like Black

Sabbath?''

And Aeronwy said politely, "To us, the kind of music we try to play, Black Sabbath is like Lawrence Welk."

"Oh."

Once Amy laughed aloud. She usually did when she recalled that time in the dim dark past when she had tried to convince Aeronwy that with the restricted audience for heavy metal, maybe she should see if she could cross over, into country and western music, say.

"You know," she had rushed on, "it's all music and you've said it yourself, people relate to that kind of music, songs about broken love affairs, memories of good times, things that happen to everyday people . . ." She'd been quite serious, based on the fact that the kid could sing any style, from sweet to sounding not unlike Janis Joplin at her sandpapery best.

Anyway, a day or two after that conversation she heard Aeronwy in the shower, singing out a kind of Tanya Tucker imitation so that her mother could hear for sure, the opening lines of her first and no doubt last country song:

"Oh, why is there always a cold spot now,

Where the wet spot used to be?"

*Christmas morning,* Amy thought, *and I'm here playing reruns of old times.*

At 4 a.m. the phone rang. Amy picked it up.

"Mom? Are you sitting down? Did you get my telegram? I tried to phone you but you weren't home yet and then I had to go out on a gig we just finished.

I've got the most wonderful news!"

"Tell me. I could use some."

But that was the last calm moment she had for a while. It wasn't a matter of making up her mind about anything because she knew instantly that this was it, that everything, all those times together, had led to this.

While Aeronwy talked, Amy could imagine her, wherever she was, with her eyes shining as the words poured out that she'd won an audition and the group had a contract with a record company and there was money up front for her and they would be playing in California for the next few months, and she'd rented a nice apartment and she wanted Amy to come there and live with her.

"You should see it, Mom, airy and big and with big windows and flowers and everything just so fantastic I can't believe it!" This was followed by a strangled, "Oh, Mom!" and Amy knew Aeronwy was crying for a minute or two. Then she said, tentatively, as if not wanting to interfere, "You could write here, Mom."

"I guess I could, at that."

"Then you'll come?"

"Yes."

They both cried a little before Aeronwy said Amy was to call the airlines right now and they said they loved each other and see you soon and Merry Christmas.

When Amy hung up the phone she paused a minute, then put on the kettle for more tea and then yelled, some kind of a wild sound of pure release, and then looked around feeling very sentimental and again close to tears, still a sharp image in her mind of that morning long ago when the kid was so little, walking in the snow in the sunshine and not watching where she was going, her eyes turned up at the sky.

# HIGHLY COLORED
# CHRISTMAS SCENES

For a couple of years now, I have been carrying around a clipping describing how a woman named Mrs. H. decorates her place at Christmas. This clipping reads as follows:

*When Mrs. H. is decorating a table-size tree for a bedroom, she raids her sewing box and jewellery box. Brightly colored thread is fastened on the branches with loops of ribbon. The garlands are long strands of beads. Pendants, earrings, necklaces, pins and brooches glitter from the branches.*

*For decorating a den, fishing lures and golf tees are suggested. Mrs. H. uses her husband's cuff links for glitter. She ingeniously shoots ribbons of his spray shaving lather along the tops of the branches and in about an hour the lather puffs up, giving a soft, fluffy effect of new snow. For stars she uses cotton swabs, wired together, the wiring concealed by a cotton ball glued at the centre and sprinkled with glitter.*

We take you now to the Hs' home for few little Christmas scenes.

SCENE ONE: The bedroom. Mr. H. is sitting in a chair reading the Racing Form. His wife has been decorating their boudoir tree and is fastening brightly colored thread on the branches with loops of ribbon. The thread leads through the tree branches and then goes around a couple of chairs and winds up in the middle of Mr. H.'s back. As we watch, Mrs. H. pulls to get a little more thread and Mr. H.'s alpaca sweater, which he received last Christmas from Santa Claus, pays out rapidly until it is no bigger than a tea-cosy.

Mrs. H. is oblivious, which, all things considered, is no upset.

Mr. H. speaks: "Hey."

Mrs. H.: "Yes, dear?"

Mr. H.: "Do you feel a draft?"

SCENE TWO: The bedroom, 20 minutes later. Mrs. H. has run out of necklaces, beads, earrings, pendants, pins and brooches and has gone down to decorate the den. She told her husband this, but he was not listening. He rises to get a sweater, wondering idly what happened to the one he had on.

He is wearing his reading glasses, so things are a little blurred. He stops in front of the boudoir Christmas tree.

Mr. H.: "What in heck are you wearing all those rocks for? I thought we were going to bed." He chuckles. "I tell you, when you get all that stuff on you look just like a Christmas tree." Pales apprehensively, knowing he has said something that might make his wife cry. Leans over and kisses Christmas tree in placatory manner. Winces, but covers manfully. Returns to chair with wry glance at audience, during which he spits out several pine needles and shrugs as if to say, "Well, and what would you do, Mac?"

SCENE THREE: The following evening. Mr. H. has just returned from a hard day at the office. Glances into kitchen, where his wife is blowing up marshmallows with a bicycle pump. She is oblivious. (That's the last time I'll say that.) He tiptoes into his study, not turning on the light, because he doesn't want anyone to know he is there. He has a bottle in the bottom drawer of his desk. After a few drinks, he notices with the aid of some passing moonlight that for some reason it is snowing shaving cream tonight.

"Ridiculush!" he asserts, but then tastes some and cringes with fear. It is his own brand! Can that be a sign?

He glances fearfully into the vaulted heavens and notices how much the stars look just like cotton swabs wired together, with the wiring concealed by a cotton ball glued at the centre and sprinkled with glitter. "Cotton swabsh!" he groans. "I'm going mad!"

He knows he should be getting home, but has forgotten his compass and cannot find the North Cotton Swab to steer by. "However, here'sh a tree," he remarks. "Mosh grows on nor shide." While circling the tree he remarks to it, with a sob, how much it reminds him of his wife. He finds no moss, but gradually his horrified eyes focus on something glittering brightly on the tree. His cuff links, fishing lures and golf tees!

"I'm dead!" he cries. "Squirrelsh have shtored my shtuff in treesh for the winter!"

He falls in a dead faint. Mrs. H. comes in a moment later, turns on the light, and piles blown-up marshmallows around him to make a snowbank.

# THE 25-CENT GIFT

One Saturday close to Christmas I cleaned out a closet to discard clothes I didn't want. One of my sons was home that day. For years during his occasional stays with us, this son has left unwanted clothes behind and these had accumulated in boxes in the basement. "I'm taking some things to the Salvation Army," I said. "How about checking your stuff and putting in what you don't want?" In the end we had quite a respectable pile. I tied it into a parcel and took it to the Salvation Army store on Richmond Street West in Toronto.

The building is fairly new and the entrance modern glass and steel. I went up a few steps from the street and turned right through another door and then I was facing the clothing part of the store. It is quite an experience if you have never been there: a room as big as a city lot, full of secondhand clothing and dotted here and there with men and women from our affluent society, looking for used clothes with a little more use left in them.

A counter runs along the south side of the room. Two women in blue smocks were chatting there sociably with people who maybe had come as much for new conversation as for used clothes.

"I have some clothes here," I said to one of the women.

"Just put them there at the end of the counter," she said.

I went on in. Here was the emptying of the city's closets. One bin as big as one of the wagon-boxes I used to drive full of wheat in threshing time on the Prairies was full of underwear and blouses, rumpled and tired from the hunt. There were racks of coats and suits and dresses, windbreakers, pants, shirts. People moved slowly among them, heads down, serious.

At the southeast corner of the clothing floor, an arrow pointed up. I followed it. On the second floor was all your one-time furniture, you people who bought new and called the Salvation Army to take away the old. Here was the city's harvest, big ugly chairs with hair grease on the back, chesterfields with grey cotton stuffing sticking up through the worn patches, piano stools painted brown (and painted 100 times). People had made love here and fought there and cried bitter, bitter tears.

And then on top of something, I don't remember what, there was this tiny high chair.

I picked it up. It stood solidly. The tray on the front would fold back over a doll's head, like a real chair. The back seemed to have been cut out of a plywood crate and there were other signs that sometime, for God knows which little girl and her dollies, someone had made this high chair from what wood he had on hand. I thought of all the shopping we had done for our own little girl, now three-and-a-half, and of all the parcels piling up for her at home.

I carried the high chair to the counter in the corner and said to a man, middle-aged or more, "I'd like to take this."

He looked at it. "Give me 25 cents," he said.

I put the little high chair in the trunk of my car, where the bale of clothes had been on the way down. I stood it up and worked the tray and inspected it more closely. It was not beautiful; it was a little squat and ugly, dirty and rough in spots, but I had the thought that it had been made with love. It had that about it still.

I kept it in the car trunk. Then I bought some sandpaper one day downtown, and a small paint brush, and found a can of turquoise enamel in the basement at home. Two days ago I smuggled it into the house and down to my workroom and spread paper on the floor and went to work.

All the time I worked I wondered how our little girl would react to it. She would walk in her own total solitude, the aloneness of the child, in her sleepers to the lighted tree. There it would be among the expensive toys she had seen on television, and had firmly asked for, so that if she followed the custom of last year she would announce with more satisfaction than surprise: "There's my tricycle, and there's my doll carriage, and there's my Trik-Trak . . ." and on and on.

I can't tell you how she did react, because this was written a little before the wild commercial scenes of Christmas morning. But I'm not stupid enough to think that her reaction is the important thing, anyway;

the important reaction was mine alone, the selfish one, at finding something I could give her that did not depend on money – except for that 25 cents.

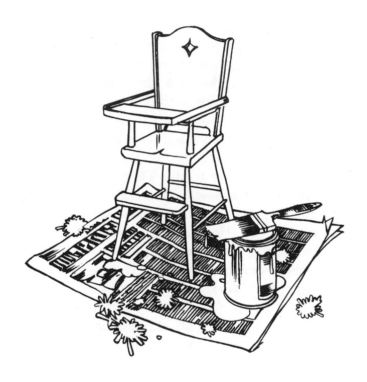

# THE SANTA SCAM

hen I arrived home this morning it was to find a scene of unparalleled chaos prevailing in the normally peaceful environs of the North Pole. I could see the crowd from a mile or two away, but thought it was only a bunch of the elves whooping it up. This they usually do on Christmas Day from a combination of an overdose of snowberry wine and the natural release after months of hard work spent helping me prepare for Christmas. I didn't even glance down again, after that one look. A couple of lousy reindeer had flaked out on me over the Belcher Islands. It was taking all my skill as a reindeer driver to get the sleigh down safe and sound on what I had left.

I was right in the front yard, yelling to my wife, "Break out the ice cubes!" when my eyelids suddenly snapped back with reports like pistol shots. Those weren't elves, they were television crews! Those men running toward me with microphones thrust out like lances, clutching tape-recorders to their bosoms, were radio reporters. And the more courtly types behind them, unsheathing their automatic quill pens, must be (by their stately mien) none other than the nation's most respected political columnists and commentators.

I knew I was in trouble, but at first I tried to gag it

HO HO HO HO

up. Until that moment I'd thought I didn't have a good ho-ho left in me, but apprehension is a great healer. I came out with a couple of dandies. Then I walked right through the crush to the guys I knew could make or break me, the columnists.

"Come Fraser! Come Newman! Come Lynch and George Bain!" I cried. "Let's go in and have a drink!"

But just stopping to say that, I lost my forward momentum and the others were on me.

"Where did you buy your furniture, Santa, after the North Pole burned down that time?" one asked, shoving a microphone into my face.

"Have you made any payments on it?" asked another.

"Is it true," asked a third, "that you have an interest in three companies that make toys, and that these companies have been getting all your contracts lately without even submitting tenders?"

"About the toys," I said indignantly. "I declared my interest at the time we were considering those contracts. The elves voted them in. I didn't say a word."

A fourth man thrust forward. "What about the report that one of your elves offered a bribe to a person or persons unknown to fight extradition proceedings against you?"

"What case is that?" I asked, stalling for time.

"The one, State of New York vs S. Claus, for knocking down TV aerials on apartment buildings!"

"Those lousy aerials!" I snapped. "I couldn't take 'em any more. All I did was take my toy bag in my hands like this" - I took my toy bag in both hands - "and then swing it like this! And this!"

If the bag had been full of toys right then, I might have bowled them over and got safely inside. But all I had left in the bag was a few bottles of booze I hadn't been able to deliver in Quebec because of the liquor board strike - and they broke along with the first television camera I hit. So there I was, still outside and surrounded.

"Is it true that you take kickbacks from Santa Clauses in department stores, in direct contravention of the Ontario Labor Code?" a woman said.

"I'd like to get back to the bribe offer," shouted another.

"I knew nothing about it!" I said.

"When did you find out about it?"

"November 24."

"An elf didn't mention it to you on September 27?"

"No!" I shouted. "Or, what I mean is, yes, but not very loudly."

"Who holds the garbage removal contracts here at the North Pole? Isn't it true you have an interest in those companies?"

"No comment," I said, wearily.

"Where do you get your funds for running this show? Isn't it true that you get them from big corporations, in return for your sanctioning their Santa Claus parades? Isn't it true that your bagman is one of your own elves?"

At this point, I had had about all I could take. I had been backing and turning until I had a clear path to the door. I did the only thing really left to me.

"Merry Christmas to all!" I cried, swinging my soggy bag menacingly around me. "And to all – drop dead!"

Then I ran for it. I made it through the door safely. But what is happening to people these days, anyway?